PATHWAYS TO SPIRITUAL UNDERSTANDING

by Dr. Richard S. Powers

HENSLEY
PUBLISHING
6116 E. 32nd St.
Tulsa, OK 74134

Dedication

I would like to dedicate this book to my mother, Mrs. Eva J. (Powers) Quesada. And to the loving memory of my father, Rev. William A. Powers, Jr. who laid down his sword and picked up his crown on May 25th, 1975. It was Dad and Mother who taught me to listen to those who were my teachers. From a young age I was instructed to, "incline my ear unto wisdom." From these many years of listening to wise men and ladies, coupled with my time in the church study, came the points and principles of this book.

ISBN 1-56322-023-7

Acknowledgments

I would like to thank the good people of the Grace Baptist Church for the many years they have faithfully followed the vision God placed upon my heart when I became their pastor in 1975. No pastor ever had sweeter people to lead and no pastor ever enjoyed his place of service any more than I do.

I also want to thank my dear wife, Brenda and our children, Richard, Melinda and Joshua, who have given a great portion of their lives to the ministry simply by association with a husband and father who is a pastor. The Bible teaches a man that when he has found a good wife he holds a treasure more valuable than rubies. In this, I am a wealthy man.

And finally, thank you to Rev. Jeff Bail and to Linda Davis. Along with my wife, these two people make up our church staff. We share a common zeal for the ministry and a love for our people that motivates us to serve one another as we serve the King of Kings.

About the Author

For years, Richard Powers has felt a special call to disciple new Christians and new church members. Because all the course material he found was either too simple or too complicated, Powers decided to write his own. The result was *Pathways to Spiritual Understanding.*

Powers, a fourth-generation pastor, received his Bachelor of Religious Education from Midwestern Baptist College in Pontiac, Michigan.

The morning after his college graduation, Powers' father suffered a fatal heart attack. A week later, young Powers followed his father's footsteps as pastor of Grace Baptist Church in Brunswick, Ohio.

That's where his following ended and his leading began.

Since that time, Grace Baptist has grown from an average Sunday morning attendance of 175 to over 700.

Powers lives in Brunswick with his wife and three children.

Preface

"For this cause we also, since the day we heard it, do not cease to pray for you, and to desire that ye might be filled with the knowledge of his will in all wisdom and spiritual understanding; That ye might walk worthy of the Lord unto all pleasing, being fruitful in every good work, and increasing in the knowledge of God." Colossians 1:9-10

The Apostle Paul wrote to the church of Colosse and told of his great burden and desire for the believers in Colosse to be filled with the knowledge of the will of God and with spiritual understanding. There was a reason behind Paul's desire. We find that reason in verse 10 of Colossians, chapter one. He wanted the believers at Colosse to know how they could "walk worthy of the Lord," to live the Christian life that would bring glory and honor to the Lord. This is the life that is pleasing to Him.

According to Paul, increasing in spiritual understanding leads one to live the life that is fruitful in every good work and increases in the knowledge of God (Colossians 1:10). That ought to be the goal of every saved person. To live a life on this earth that reflects the life of Christ in such measure that others see the effects of salvation and have a desire to know the One who can change lives in such a wonderful way!

There is a story told concerning the conqueror Alexander the Great. It is said that one day an unruly soldier was brought to stand before Alexander to answer charges of misconduct and disrespect. As the list of charges was recited, the great leader began to grow more and more irritated that a soldier in his army would act in such a manner. When the last charge of misconduct was read, Alexander asked the soldier his name. There was a long pause. Then the accused man replied, "My name is Alexander."

Upon hearing this, Alexander the Great rose from his chair, looked directly into the eyes of the offending soldier and issued this order: "Soldier! Either change your conduct, or change your name!" I wonder how many times the Lord is grieved when we do not live a life that is "worthy of His name."

In II Corinthians 5:20 we read, "Now then we are ambassadors for Christ...." The purpose of the Christian's life is to be a representative of the Lord. No ambassador of the United States is sent on a mission for his nation without first receiving the training that equips him to be the best possible representative of this great country. Yet many have been saved who did not follow their salvation with training that would equip them to be a good ambassador for Christ. That is the purpose for this course of study!

This course is designed to help you increase in "the knowledge of God and spiritual understanding." As you do, you will experience a wonderful transformation in your Christian life. For, as the Bible says, you will be "strengthened with all might, according to his glorious power unto all patience and longsuffering with joyfulness" (Colossians 1:11). The life of a good ambassador is the life of joy and patience. The Lord has reserved special

AUTHOR'S STUDY NOTE

Throughout the enclosed outlines you will find four or five verses assigned to each lesson. Begin a systematic plan for Scripture memorization using these weekly verses as a place to start. I recommend the plan that I have used over the years to commit portions of God's Word to memory.

Place one verse of Scripture from your weekly list on each side of a 3 x 5 index card. To memorize four or five verses weekly, you will need only two or three cards at the most. Read your verses aloud at least five times in the morning and again at least five times in the evening, before retiring for the night. In addition, carry your cards in your pocket or purse and promise the Lord that you will give Him your "waiting" time throughout the day.

We all spend quite some time each day waiting at traffic lights, in line at the bank, at the check-out counter, or in any number of other situations. Rather than become agitated during those situations where you are forced to wait, use that time in a wonderful, constructive manner. What could benefit a Christian more than investing that time in Scripture memory? When you find yourself waiting during the day, just take the 3 x 5 cards out and go over your weekly verses as often as time allows. By adding this to the time spent morning and evening each day, you'll find that by the end of the week you will have those verses firmly in your mind.

At the end of the week don't

blessings for those who will invest the time to learn how to "walk worthy of the Lord unto all pleasing."

It has been my burden for many years of pastoring that God's people grow in their faith to spiritual maturity. Far too many are "born again" but do not grow beyond spiritual infancy. Our Lord, in His great commission, commanded not only that we win others to Christ, but that we also teach them to observe all things that He commanded. We must, therefore, couple our evangelistic endeavors with some teaching of the basic tenants of the Christian life. This course will cover those areas. We must help lay a good foundation for the Christian who wants to "increase in spiritual understanding" and learn to be a good ambassador for Christ.

If you are studying this course in a classroom atmosphere, be faithful in your attendance. Remember, it was Sunday night when Jesus came to visit His disciples after the resurrection and Thomas was not among them (John 20:19-25). Thomas missed out on the blessings of seeing the Lord because, for some reason, he skipped the meeting! It is often true that the lesson you miss will be the one that you would have enjoyed most. Be faithful and don't miss out on the blessings!

God bless you as you walk along the pathways to spiritual understanding which will bring you into the fruitful life of a good ambassador of Christ.

Dr. Richard S. Powers
Author

toss the cards out, rather keep them for review once or twice during the next week. In a short time this system will become a good spiritual habit in your life and Scripture memorization will become a blessing!

Just think what a difference it could make in your life if you would commit to memory just two or three verses every week. Using this plan, anyone can memorize 100 to 200 verses of God's Word each year. The Bible says in Psalm 119:11, "Thy word have I hid in mine heart, that I might not sin against thee." There is no better defense for the believer against the temptations of the devil than the verses of God's Word that are committed to memory.

May God bless you as you endeavor to make memorization of His precious Word a part of your daily life and your daily walk as a good "ambassador of Christ."

Table of Contents

About Photocopying This Book

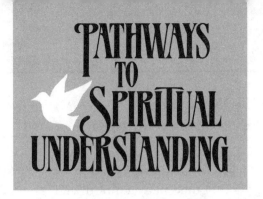

PATHWAYS TO SPIRITUAL UNDERSTANDING

LESSON 1

The Natural Man

MAIN SCRIPTURES:
GENESIS 1:26-27; GENESIS 2:7-9, & 16-17;
GENESIS 3:1-8; GENESIS 6:5-12

LESSON AIM: To lead to a Biblical understanding of how mankind came to populate the earth. To learn how God made man and how man fell from God's grace. To teach that the effects of that fall brought sin into the world, and that the sin nature is passed from generation to generation. To lead to the understanding that, according to the Bible, the natural man is the unsaved man.

SUGGESTED MEMORY VERSES:
Genesis 2:7; Genesis 6:12; I Corinthians 15:44; I Corinthians 15:49 and I Corinthians 2:14

OVERVIEW:

   I. WHAT IS THE DEFINITION OF *LIFE?*

   II. WHERE DID LIFE COME FROM?

   III. HOW MANY KINDS OF LIFE ARE THERE?

   IV. WHAT IS THE LENGTH OF LIFE?

   V. WHAT IS THE PURPOSE OF LIFE?

   VI. WHY WOULD SOME, STILL IN THE NATURAL STATE, NOT USE THEIR TIME TO PREPARE FOR ETERNITY?

INTRODUCTION: Many years ago Nehru, of India, was a guest in the United States. During his tour, he asked to visit with Albert Einstein, the famous scientist. Near the end of his visit, Nehru turned to Einstein and asked, "Mr. Einstein, you have been called the greatest brain that ever lived; but have you discovered the purpose and the meaning of life?" It is said that Mr. Einstein bowed his head and softly replied, "No, I have not yet found the meaning to my life."

Certain questions have troubled mankind for thousands of years. "Where did I come from?" "Why am I here?" "Where am I going?" "What is the purpose of my life?" These questions are the reason for this lesson on understanding the natural man.

(Where lines are provided after a Scripture reference, look up the verse and write a one sentence summary of what this Scripture is saying to you.)

1

I. WHAT IS THE DEFINITION OF LIFE?

A.   Did you ever try to give a comprehensive definition of
life?
Truth is, it's a difficult thing to define. Some say life is
the state of being alive. That's true, but too vague.
Others say life is the period of time between birth and
death. This is offensive to the Christian, who believes
that life begins before birth and continues after physical
death.

B.   The Bible gives a simple, yet profound definition of life.
James 4:14 says, *"Life is a vapour, that appeareth for
a little time, and then vanisheth away."*
According to the Bible then, life is just a short span of
conscious existence upon this earth — "a little time." It's
a precious gift from God, so fragile it can be here today
and gone tomorrow!

II. WHERE DID LIFE COME FROM?

A.   God is the creator and the source of all life.
Your life came from your parents, who got theirs from
their parents, and so on, all the way back to Genesis 2:7
where we learn that God created Adam and Eve—our
original parents. (John 1:1-4) _____

_____

_____

B.   God made man in His image; but what does that mean?
God is a trinity (3 parts being One). And God made
man in trinity fashion (3 parts that make up one whole
man). The trinity of man is taught in I Thessalonians
5:23: *"And the very God of peace sanctify you wholly;
and I pray God your whole spirit and soul and body
be preserved blameless unto the coming of our Lord
Jesus Christ."*

1.   *Man is made with a* **body.**
    a.   God designed and made man's body according
        to a plan. (Psalm 139:14)
    b.   Man was created perfect and sinless in his
        original state.
    c.   The body of man began it's "march to the
        grave" when he sinned against God.
        (Genesis 2:17)
    d.   Sin brought such things as weakness, sickness,
        pain and suffering.
    e.   At salvation, the body doesn't get saved. The
        body is part of the natural man. It will
        eventually die and go back to the dust of the
        ground from which it came.

2.   Man is made with a *spirit.*
    a.   Many believe the soul and the spirit are the
        same thing, yet the Bible teaches us they are
        separate and divisible. (Hebrews 4:12)

    b.   The spirit of man is the center of our intellect. It controls our will and our actions.

    c.   In the Bible, the words "heart" and "spirit" are often used synonomously.

    d.   It's in the spirit (or heart) of man that sin finds it's beginnings. (Mark 7:21-23)

    e.   It's also in the heart of man that salvation begins. (Romans 6:17-18) Outward reformation doesn't last without a change in one's heart.

    f.   The natural man's spirit is difficult to control since he doesn't have the indwelling help of the Holy Spirit. He doesn't think properly, because his heart (spirit) isn't right with God.

    g.   The spirit of man, unlike the body, is eternal and will not die.

In summary, the spirit is the center of personality. It controls decisions and actions.

    3.   Man is made with a *soul.*

    a.   God breathed into man, and man became a living soul. (Genesis 2:7)

    b.   The soul is an eternal part of man that will not die.

    c.   The soul is the seat of all affections, emotions and desires.

    d.   It's the soul that coordinates the thoughts and activities of the body and the spirit.

    e.   The soul is the inner man, the complete make-up of one's self.

    f.   Christ died to redeem man's soul. (Hebrews 10:39)

    g.   The soul and the spirit depart the body at death for either Heaven or Hell.

    h.   The soul of the natural man is *not* redeemed. It can never see Heaven without the new birth. (John 3:3)

    i.   The Bible warns the natural man concerning the great value of his soul. (Mark 8:36) _____

_____

_____

III. HOW MANY KINDS OF LIFE ARE THERE?

Basically, there are three distinctive types of life taught in the Bible.

    A.   There is *physical* life.

    1.   This life begins at conception and ends at death.

    2.   It's the only life that the natural man has.

    3.   As long as the soul and the spirit remain in the body, there is physical life.

    B.   There is *spiritual* life.

    1.   This life begins at salvation and changes the lifestyle of the natural man. (II Corinthians 5:17) _____

_____

_____

2.   It's the abundant life. (John 10:10)
3.   It begins with a "spiritual birth."

C.   There is *eternal* life.
1.   This life begins at the new birth and will never end! (John 10:28)
2.   Natural man doesn't possess eternal life, nor does he possess the benefits of salvation, which include the indwelling of the Holy Spirit.
3.   Since the natural man doesn't possess the indwelling Spirit, he doesn't understand spiritual things. (I Corinthians 2:14)

IV. WHAT IS THE LENGTH OF LIFE?

A.   The natural man's lifespan has continued to decrease since God created man.

1.   Adam lived 930 years.
   a.   The average lifespan of man in the days before the flood was 846 years.
   b.   After the great flood, the lifespan of the natural man decreased to average only 393 years. (Genesis 11)
2.   Abraham, who lived 20 generations later, lived only 175 years.
3.   According to Psalm 90, written by Moses in his day, the average lifespan was considered to be 70 years. A long life was 80 years. (This is about average today.)

B.   The point of the matter is: Life is limited to a short time on earth, at best.

1.   Job 7:1 teaches us that God, in His sovereign will, has established the span of life for every person.
2.   The natural man is warned to prepare to meet God quickly, for he has no assurance of the length of his days. (Proverbs 27:1) _____

_____

_____

V. WHAT IS THE PURPOSE OF LIFE?

A.   Life is but a brief moment of time in which to prepare for eternity. If you succeed in all other areas of life and fail in this preparation, your life will have been wasted. (Mark 8:36-37)

B.   You've been placed upon this earth to personally choose the abiding place of your soul and spirit after they depart the natural body.
   Jesus taught only two final destinations in the Gospel of Matthew 7:13-14 _____

_____

_____

VI. WHY WOULD SOME STILL IN THE NATURAL STATE NOT USE THEIR TIME TO PREPARE FOR ETERNITY?

It's difficult to understand, but many people don't prepare to meet God — for various reasons.

A. There are several categories of people found in the ranks of the natural man.

1. Some won't be saved because they're *neglectors.*

   a. Hebrews 2:3 asks a great question of all who are neglectors. *"How shall we escape if we neglect so great salvation?"*

   b. It has been said, "The road to Hell is paved with the stones of procrastination."

2. Some won't be saved because they're *rejectors.*

   a. Many go about trying to establish their own righteousness and feel they are good enough to go to Heaven as they are. (Romans 10:1-3)

   _____

   _____

   b. They reject Christ as the way to forgiveness of sins and will die still in the natural, or unsaved, state.

3. Some won't be saved because they're *mockers.*
   a. Mockers despise and make light of the Bible's plan for man's salvation.
   b. The Apostle Paul had mockers in a crowd to whom he was preaching. (Acts 17:32)

4. Some won't be saved because they're *pretenders.*
   a. Pretenders are those who know they haven't been saved, but continue to put on a "front" of Christianity before others.
   b. A pretender named Simon is found in Acts 8:9-23. He passed himself off before others as a great man of God, when in reality, he had never been converted.

B. The natural man does not have Christ as his Savior.

1. The natural man has no spiritual life at all.

2. Unless he is born again, he will never see Heaven.
   a. II Corinthians 6:2 says, *"Behold, now is the accepted time; behold, now is the day of salvation."*
   b. The life of the natural man may end at any moment.
   c. It's imperative that you see this great salvation offered freely through Christ Jesus and without delay choose to trust Him as your Lord and Savior.
   d. In so doing, you'll move from the category of the natural man into the category of the

spiritual man and be ready to grow in this wonderful new life!

SUMMARY: The purpose of this lesson has been to study man in his "natural" state. That is, the way he enters the world through "natural birth." Jesus said in John 3:6, *"That which is born of the flesh is flesh; and that which is born of the Spirit is spirit."* The Lord was teaching us that there's a natural birth that takes place when we're born of the flesh into the family of man. Likewise, there's a spiritual birth that takes place when one is born the second time, by faith, into the family of God.

The natural man is without Christ as his Savior and, therefore, has no indwelling Holy Spirit to guide and convict. Since he doesn't possess the Holy Spirit, he lives to please himself. He'll do the desires of the flesh. His attempts at self-reformation will be fruitless until he's first saved by the grace of God.

It's normal that the natural man doesn't understand the Bible or matters of doctrine. These things are alien to his nature. It takes the new birth and the indwelling Spirit to begin to be successful in the study of the Word of God. Therefore, those who desire to witness to the unsaved (those in the natural realm) must resist the urge to argue doctrine, and must keep pointing the unsaved person to Christ, who is able to save and change lives. For, *"if any man be made in Christ, he is a new creature."* (II Corinthians 5:17).

REFLECTIONS: Answer the following questions individually or in class. Give careful attention to your answers. This exercise is what the Bible refers to as *meditation.* Think on these things....

1. What's a simple, yet concise definition of life?

   _____

   _____

2. Why is it so important to know and be convinced that God is the creator of all life?

   _____

   _____

3. What does the Bible mean when it says God made man in His image?

   _____

   _____

4. When does physical life begin? (Be careful!)

   _____

   _____

5. How can one know that he or she has passed from natural life to spiritual life? Are there evidences?

   _____

   _____

6. Why do the unsaved find the Bible difficult to understand?

   _____

   _____

7. What are some of the things that keep the unsaved from salvation?

   _____

   _____

8. What are we told in the Bible about the length of our natural life on earth?

   _____

   _____

9. What are some of the reasons for the decrease in man's natural lifespan on earth since his creation?

   _____

   _____

10. What should be the main concern of the natural man?

    _____

    _____

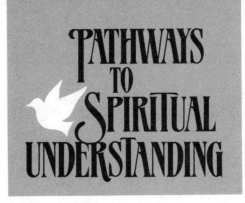

PATHWAYS TO SPIRITUAL UNDERSTANDING

LESSON 2

Margin of Error

The New Birth

MAIN SCRIPTURES:
JOHN 3:1-18; EPHESIANS 2:8-10;
ROMANS 10:9-13

LESSON AIM: To lead to a Biblical understanding of the new birth, or what it means to be saved. To learn how God planned for man's salvation. To learn how to share what it means to be born again with others.

SUGGESTED MEMORY VERSES:
John 3:16; John 3:3; John 10:9; Romans 3:23; Romans 6:23; Romans 10:13

OVERVIEW:

I. THE GREATEST NECESSITY — THE NEW BIRTH

II. HOW CAN WE BE BORN AGAIN?

III. NEW THINGS ONE CAN EXPECT AS A RESULT OF THE NEW BIRTH

INTRODUCTION: The *new birth* is the greatest of all man's needs. Jesus said so in John, chapter 3, to a man named Nicodemus.

In verse 3, the Lord told Nicodemus that unless he were to be born again he would never see the kingdom of God. In simple terms Jesus said, "Nicodemus, you must be saved in order to go to Heaven." Therefore, this new birth becomes the greatest of all human needs!

If a sick man gets well, that's good; but it will only last a short time. If an ignorant man becomes educated, that's also good; but his education will only benefit him a short time. If a poor man achieves great wealth, even that will only last a short time. But, when a man meets Christ as Savior, his life will be changed forever! Let's examine what the Bible has to say about how a man can be born again and become a child of God.

(Where lines are provided after a Scripture reference, look up the verse and write a one sentence summary of what this Scripture is saying to you.)

You were not an accident
What drive your life
2 resentment
and anger/forgivness
3 fear/unbealethi
4 Materialism
5 approval

Know
your purpose
Made to last
forever

1 Guelt/lives
spent runny
Manipulated by
Memories

9

I. THE GREATEST NECESSITY—THE NEW BIRTH

A. How do we know that this is the greatest of all necessities?

1. Because Jesus said so in John 3:3 when He declared there is simply no other way to Heaven other than the new birth.

2. Because Jesus was speaking to Nicodemus.
   a. No finer man, in human terms, had ever stood before the Lord Jesus than Nicodemus.
   b. He was a Pharisee, meaning he was good, honest, moral and religious.

3. Because of the term Jesus used.
   a. He said, *"Ye MUST be born again."*
   b. When Jesus, the Son of God, uses the word "must," it's a Divine "must." There is no way around it.
   c. The Lord wasn't offering a suggestion, or making a recommendation. He was stating a fact.
   d. If you plan to see Heaven, ***You Must Be Born Again!***

If a man like Nicodemus *must* be born again to see the kingdom of God, that means that you and I must also.

II. HOW CAN WE BE BORN AGAIN?

A. This is the very question Nicodemus asked Jesus when he said, in John 3:4, *"How can this happen?"*

1. As religious as Nicodemus was, he came to Jesus seeking some inner peace.
   a. Therefore, we conclude that religion alone can't produce peace with God.
   b. Knowing that Nicodemus was a Pharisee and his life was, no doubt, full of good works, we can further conclude that good works won't produce peace with God.
   c. Only through salvation by faith does one find real peace with God! (Romans 5:1) _____

   _____

   _____

2. The new birth isn't *physical* birth but *spiritual* birth. (John 3:6) _____

   _____

   _____

B. The single greatest verse in the Bible, John 3:16, has much to tell us of this wonderful salvation.

1. It tells of a wonderful love! (*"For God so loved the world..."*)
   a. God's love is wonderful because of its outreach. God loves the world. (every nation,

every state, every county, every town, every village, every person). When God loved, He loved the whole world.

b. God's love is wonderful because of what it does. His love delivers from sin, changes lives, heals broken hearts, mends broken homes, lifts the fallen, and provides salvation for the lost. (I John 3:1) _____

_____

_____

2. It tells of a wonderful gift! *("...that He gave His only begotten Son....")*
   a. This gift is wonderful because of what Jesus did for us. He gave Himself to die in our place, and as the substitute for our guilt. (I Peter 3:18)
   b. This gift is wonderful because the price for it has already been paid in full. (Romans 6:23) __

_____

_____

   c. This gift is wonderful because it proves God's great love for us. Love is measured by what it gives.
   d. This gift is wonderful because the giver is God, Himself.

3. It tells of a wonderful plan! *("...that whosoever believeth in Him should not perish...")*
   a. This salvation plan is wonderful because of its simplicity. (Ephesians 2:8-9 and Titus 3:5) ____

_____

_____

   Simply believing and receiving by faith is what God requires. (Acts 16:30-31)
   b. This salvation plan is wonderful because it's available to everyone— *"For whosoever..."* Thank God for that wonderful little word "whosoever." It leaves no one out. (II Peter 3:9, I Timothy 2:3-4 and John 10:9) _____

_____

_____

   c. This salvation plan is wonderful because of what it saves us from. *("...should not perish...")* It saves us from eternity in the only Scriptural alternative to Heaven — Hell. (Luke 13:3) ____

_____

_____

4. It tells of a wonderful life! ("...but have everlasting life.")

11

    a.   Salvation brings eternal life to all who receive Christ as Savior.

    b.   This life isn't dependent upon good works, or any other merit, but upon the grace of God.

    c.   This life will never end. (John 10:28) _____

_____

_____

    d.   The daily life of one who has been born again ought to be characterized by joy and peace of mind. (John 15:11)

    e.   It's a *wonderful life* that begins when you accept this *wonderful gift* offered by the *wonderful love* of a *wonderful God*.

III. NEW THINGS ONE CAN EXPECT AS A RESULT OF THE NEW BIRTH

    A.   When an individual is saved, he becomes a new *creature*. (II Corinthians 5:17)

        1.   This produces a new *life*.
            This new life is to be lived in such a way as to bring glory to the Lord. (Galatians 2:20) _____

_____

_____

        2.   This produces a new *love*.
            a.   We're to love the Lord. (I John 4:19) _____

_____

_____

            b.   We're to love one another. (I John 4:11) _____

_____

_____

        3.   This produces new *longings*.
            a.   The Apostle Paul's great desire after he was converted was to know the Lord better. (Philippians 3:10)
            b.   Our longing ought to be to know Him better every day so that we can learn to live more like Him.

        4.   This produces a new *"looking."*
            The world looks for things like wealth, power, goods and fame; but the Christian is to look for the Lord's return. (Titus 2:13) _____

_____

_____

    B.   When an individual is saved, he finds new *company*.

        1.   He has a new *Father*. (John 1:12) _____

_____

　　　　As with any child his desire should now be to please his Father.

2.　He has a new *family*. (Matthew 23:8) _____

　　_____

　　_____

　　a.　We're all brothers and sisters in Christ.
　　b.　The church must become more than just a people with whom to fellowship: the church must become like a family.

3.　He has new *friends*. (II Corinthians 6:17) _____

　　_____

　　_____

　　　　The new birth brings one into a whole new world of friendships with the people of God.

C.　When an individual is saved, he develops a new *character*. Four things are involved:

1.　There are new *actions*. (Galatians 5:16) _____

　　_____

　　_____

　　　　We're to *walk in the Spirit*, which means we're to allow the Lord to control and govern our actions.

2.　There are new *attitudes*. (I Corinthians 6:20) ____

　　_____

　　_____

　　　　We're told in the Bible that we should bring glory to God even in our spirit (our temperament and attitude).

3.　There are new *ambitions*. (John 6:27) _____

　　_____

　　_____

　　　　When one is saved, there should be a natural desire to become involved in the Lord's work. (Matthew 6:33)

4.　There are new *affections*. (Colossians 3:2) _____

　　_____

　　_____

　　　　Salvation produces a love for spiritual things, such as the Bible, prayer, and attending church.

D.　When an individual gets saved, there should be new *conversation*. (Ephesians 4:29)

1.　The speech of a Christian should always honor and please the Lord.
　　a.　Gossip and talebearing have no place in the

new life of a child of God. (Proverbs 26:22 and Proverbs 26:20)

b. Psalm 19:14 is a good verse to memorize and use to begin each new day. _____

_____

_____

E. When an individual is saved, he will find some new area of life to control. There are three areas of life you can learn to control with the Lord's help.

1. Control your *time.* (Colossians 4:5) _____

_____

a. Time is far too precious to waste. Learn to invest it wisely and spend it carefully.
b. God is the giver of all our time; therefore, we ought not be selfish in giving Him a portion of our time.

2. Control your *temper.* (Psalm 37:8) _____

_____

a. Temperance, or self-control, is part of the fruit of the Spirit listed in Galatians 5:22-23.
b. The child of God can expect the help of the Holy Spirit in the area of temper control.

3. Control *temptations.* (I Corinthians 10:13) _____

_____

a. All sin begins first as a temptation.
b. If one can learn to control the temptations that come daily, one can learn to avoid the *"sin which doth so easily beset us."*
c. When temptation comes, stop and pray, asking God to make the way of escape for you as He promised.

F. When one is saved there will be new *compassion!*

1. He will love the house of God. (Psalm 122:1)
2. He will love the Word of God. (Psalm 119:24, 47)
3. He will love the people of God. (John 13:34-35)
4. He will love those who are lost without Christ, and their salvation will be his desire. (This was the primary desire of the Apostle Paul, as recorded in Romans 10:1.)

SUMMARY: We may best sum up the new birth and salvation by the use of several prepositions. First, we're saved **by** something. That, of course, is God's grace. Salvation comes as the gift of God, not through our own works.

We are saved **through** something. That's our faith. To be saved apart from our faith in Christ as the only Savior is impossible. According to Hebrews 11:6, faith pleases God, and belief in Christ and His saving work pleases Him most. Salvation doesn't come through man, through church or through good works. Salvation comes by grace through faith.

We are saved **from** something. That something is sin. Matthew 1:21 says of Jesus that He shall *"save His people from their sins."* Christ died so that you may be saved by grace, through faith, from the destructive force called sin. We're told in Romans 5:20, *"Where sin abounded, grace did much more abound."* That means there's no sinner too corrupt to be saved.

Last, we're saved **for** something. That's to serve the Lord. Read Romans 6:18 and you'll see that the Lord has saved us and set us free from sin so that we might serve Him. Paul tells us in Romans 7:6 that we're to *"serve in newness of spirit."* This new birth brings a new purpose to one's life — WE ARE SAVED THAT WE MAY SERVE THE KING OF KINGS.

REFLECTIONS: Answer the following questions individually or in class. Give careful attention to your answers. This exercise is what the Bible refers to as *meditation*. Think on these things....

1. Think for a few minutes about Nicodemus of John, chapter 3. List the qualities of his character.

   _____

   _____

2. What was necessary in order for Nicodemus to "see" the Kingdom of God? What does that tell us?

   _____

3. What kind of birth is the second birth? When is one born again?

   _____

   _____

4. According to Ephesians 2:8 and 9, what cannot bring salvation? For what purpose have we been saved (according to verse 10)?

   _____

   _____

5. Think of the things necessary for the growth and development of a newborn baby. Relate that to the person who has just been saved.

   _____

   _____

6. What products should the new birth bring to one's life? (What effects that others can see?)

   _____

   _____

7. Repentance is a very necessary part of the new birth. What, then, does it mean to repent?

_____

_____

8. List four or five Bible verses that you would use in order to explain to someone how to be born again.

_____

_____

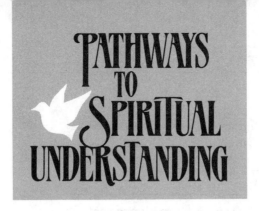

LESSON 3

The Security of the Believer

MAIN SCRIPTURES:
I JOHN 5:1-13; I PETER 1:1-5;
COLOSSIANS 2:6-13

LESSON AIM: To remove the devilish device of *doubting* when it comes to the matter of salvation. To lead to an understanding of the wonderful doctrine of the believer's security in Christ. To lead to the life of peace and joy that comes when one understands that salvation is eternal.

SUGGESTED MEMORY VERSES: I John 5:13; Colossians 2:8-9; John 10:28; Jude 24 and 25.

OVERVIEW:

   I. A CHANGED LIFE

   II. THE INDWELLING SPIRIT

   III. GOD'S WRITTEN WORD

   IV. DESIRE TO PLEASE GOD

   V. CHASTENING

   VI. AFFECTION FOR GOD'S PEOPLE

   VII. COMPLETION IN CHRIST

INTRODUCTION: Doubt has become the plague of modern-day society. People live in a world filled with doubts about the security of their jobs, the faithfulness of their spouses, their abilities as parents and even doubts about the future and what it holds.

There's one doubt, however, that the Christian needn't live under. That's the doubt of his salvation. Satan loves to sow the seeds of doubt in the hearts and minds of God's people. If he can cause them to doubt their salvation he'll cause them to become easily discouraged, and a discouraged Christian is useless to the Lord's work.

The life of a doubter is characterized by instability in his Christian life. He's on a "mountain top" one day and in a "valley" the next. There is no lasting joy and peace in the life of one who struggles with doubts about salvation. Thank God we don't have to live captivated by doubts. God said in His Word, in I John 5:13, that He has written to us so we might know that we've been saved.

If you studied the previous lesson on the new birth, and are trusting what you learned in that lesson for your salvation, then you need to study this lesson carefully to learn to rid yourself of the discouraging shadow of doubt. In this lesson you'll see seven evidences of salvation. Examine your life now in light of these Biblical evidences of salvation.

(Where lines are provided after a Scripture reference, look up the verse and write a one sentence summary of what this Scripture is saying to you.)

I.   A CHANGED LIFE

A.   When Christ enters a life and brings salvation, this salvation produces a changed life. (II Corinthians 5:17)

_____

_____

1.   This change brings an internal evidence that one has been truly saved.
   a.   The above verse says, *"...if any man be in Christ..."* It is only *in* Christ that one's life will produce this permanent change.
   b.   The verse also says *any man.* Salvation produces this change in the life of everyone who is born again.

2.   Consider the evidence found in Acts 16, in the Bible story of the Philippian jailer.
   a.   Notice his lack of concern for Paul and Silas in verses 23-27. (This is before he was saved.)
      He didn't care that they had been beaten. When they were given to his charge, he cast them into the inner prison, locked them into stocks, and went outside to sleep.
   b.   In verses 30-33, we find that he wanted to be saved—and he was. Now, note how he has changed.
      1.   He brought the two missionaries to his own house.
      2.   He washed their wounds.
      3.   He was baptized.
      4.   He gave Paul and Silas a meal.
      5.   He rejoiced with his family.
   This wonderful change in his character, his nature, his attitudes, and his actions came after he was saved. It was the natural result of the new-birth experience in his life.
3.   It's a fruitless endeavor for the unsaved to try and change old habits, old attitudes, or actions without first being saved.
   a.   This change can and will come as a result of Biblical salvation!
   b.   The realization that a change has taken place helps lead to the assurance that one has truly been saved.
   c.   Salvation produces a change in the life of all who come to Christ and are saved.

II.   GOD'S WRITTEN WORD

A.   No one can be saved apart from a belief that the Bible is the Word of an almighty God.

1.   John 5:24 _____

_____

_____

Note, "he that *heareth my word, and believeth...*"
Salvation begins with the Word of God.

2. I Peter 1:23 _____

_____

_____

The Bible is God's incorruptible seed; therefore,
it's perfect and holy.

B. This perfect and holy Book was written to give us
assurance that salvation is forever secure in Christ.

1. God's Word is His written contract concerning
salvation. (I John 5:13) _____

_____

_____

a. God wrote these things to us so we might
know that we have eternal (everlasting) life.
b. Even on those days when you may not *feel*
saved, you can *know* that you are saved by
putting your confidence in God's written
Word.
c. Salvation should never be based upon feelings,
but always upon faith.

2. The Christian can count on the promises of Jesus
when he is tempted to doubt. (John 10:28) _____

_____

_____

This is God's promise.

III. THE INDWELLING SPIRIT

A. When you are saved, the Holy Spirit moves in and makes
His abode in your life.

1. Romans 8:9 _____

_____

_____

2. The Holy Spirit indwells every saved person. We
know that we abide in Him and He in us by the
Spirit, which He gives us. (I John 3:24 and I John
4:13) _____

_____

_____

B. The Holy Spirit gives evidence of salvation.

1. He convicts by His presence, which we can sense.
(Romans 8:16) _____

_____

_____

2. He convicts us of the sin in our life, and continues

to do so until we confess and forsake it.

a. (John 16:7-8) _____

_____

_____

(*reprove* means to *convict*)

b. One who has truly been saved will always be convicted when he sins.

3. He is present to comfort us. John 14:16-17 teaches that He dwells in us to be our comforter. This presence within is evidence of our salvation.

C. We're to "walk in the Spirit," according to Galatians 5:16-17.

1. Walking in the Spirit is a daily dependence upon the Holy Spirit to lead and direct our lives.
   a. We ought to learn to include the Holy Spirit in our prayer lives.
   b. It isn't wrong to pray to the Holy Spirit seeking comfort or direction.

2. According to verse 17, walking in the Spirit produces an inner struggle between the old nature and the new nature.
   a. This struggle between the flesh and the Spirit is an evidence of the new birth.
   b. If you hadn't been saved you wouldn't have an inner struggle; therefore, it's a good indicator of salvation and should be taken as another evidence that leads to assurance.

IV. DESIRE TO PLEASE GOD

A. When one is saved, there's a desire to please the Heavenly Father that's as real as the desire of a child to please his father or mother.

1. There will be a willingness to follow God's Word and to do His commands.
   a. Read I John 2:3-5. Verse 3 tells us that this desire to keep His commandments is the way we can *know* that we know Him.
   b. We may not always do what God commands, but the desire of the heart of one who is saved is to do them.

2. The Philippian jailer in Acts, chapter 16 had this desire to please the Lord and keep His commandments.
   a. Acts 16:33 teaches us that the same night of his conversion, the jailer was baptized.
   b. This act is evidence of his desire to live in obedience to the Lord and to please Him.

B. When one doesn't have the desire to obey and to please the Lord, there's good reason for that person to have doubts about his salvation.

20

1. That is not to say that those who are saved always obey and always live to please the Lord, but that there should be an *internal desire* to do so.
   a. John 14:15 _____

   _____

   _____

   b. The proof of our love for the Lord is the way we keep His commandments.
   c. According to I John 5:3, His commandments are not grievous to a child of God.
      That is, they won't seem like a great burden.

2. Those who are saved will sense this desire to live for the Lord's glory.
   This desire is natural for all saved people. It is produced by the indwelling Spirit as another evidence of salvation.

V. CHASTENING

A. A sure sign of sonship is God's dealing with our persistent sinning. This is called chastening.

   1. In Hebrews 12:5-11, the word means "child-train."

   2. Chastening is an act of love by the Heavenly Father for His own children. (Hebrews 12:6)

   3. Chastening for sins that remain unconfessed is God's way of dealing with us as His sons. (Hebrews 12:7) _____

   _____

   _____

   4. Chastening is another strong evidence that we have truly been saved.

B. A lack of God's chastening hand in the lives of those who claim to be saved, yet persist to live in sin, should be seen as an indicator that he has most likely not been saved.

   1. Hebrews 12:8 clearly teaches that all *true* sons will be chastened by God for living in disobedience and rebellion. Those without chastisement are not true sons of God.

   2. Since God is a God of mercy and patience, His chastening may tarry a long season. His chastening will always be in an order from mild to severe.
      a. His chastening will begin first as the still small voice of the Holy Spirit as He strives to convict internally. This is God's rebuke of our sins.
      b. If that conviction is ignored, God will chasten according to Hebrews 12:6. This chastening may come in many forms.
      c. The last step in God's chastening, according to verse 6, is called *scourging,* and it is serious.

      d.   This, then, is why it's important to listen to the convicting voice of the indwelling Holy Spirit. He lives within, to keep us right with our Heavenly Father.

C.   God's chastening is for our good.

    1.   Hebrews 12:11 _____

        _____

        _____

        This is good in that it keeps us from going too far into sin, where we would be injured.

    2.   It also gives us another evidence that we are God's children.

VI. AFFECTION FOR GOD'S PEOPLE

A.   All who are saved belong to God's family. It's natural that those who belong to the same family love one another.

    1.   I John 3:14 _____

        _____

        _____

        a.   We know that we have passed from death (the life of the unsaved) to life (the life of the saved) if we love one another.
        b.   According to I John 3:18-19, this love for other Christians will "assure our hearts," or in simple terms, lead us to the heartfelt assurance that we are saved.

    2.   Notice how this love became evident in the life of the jailer at Philippi after he was converted. Acts 16:33-34 says he treated Paul and Silas with tender care and hospitality, as one would his own family. This is wonderful evidence of the saving grace of God at work in his life that night.

    3.   This love is to be shown rather than just spoken. (I John 3:17-18) _____

        _____

        _____

        a.   Love in "word and tongue" is just spoken.
        b.   Love in "deed and in truth" is that which is put into action by deeds for others. It can be seen.
        c.   Love for the brethren brings the assurance of our salvation.

    4.   Do you have this wonderful feeling of affection toward God's people? Do you enjoy their company and fellowship? If you do, then thank the Lord for another tremendous evidence of salvation at work in your heart and life.

VII. COMPLETION IN CHRIST

A. Read Colossians 2:6-13. Scripture teaches that we who are saved are *complete in Christ.* That's a great Bible truth!

    1. If something is complete, nothing more can possibly be added.

    2. *Complete in Christ* means that there is nothing that needs to be added to one who is trusting Jesus as Savior. Our salvation is complete in Him! (Not of ourselves; but all of Him!)

B. There are three reasons we know we are complete in Christ.

    1. Because of His ability to save.
        a. Acts 4:12 _____

        _____

        _____

        b. True salvation can be found in none other than Christ.
        c. He is able to save anyone who will come to Him for salvation! (Hebrews 7:25) The word "uttermost," in Hebrews 7:25, means "to the most vile offender."
        d. When we "get saved," we are as saved as we will ever be! (One ought to grow in the faith, but that is another matter entirely).
        e. Salvation isn't a slow process, but an instant new birth that comes at the moment we, by faith, accept Christ Jesus as our Savior and only hope of Heaven.
        f. Our salvation is *complete* in Him.

    2. Because He is able to keep us saved.
        a. Our salvation is in three tenses.
            1. We have been saved from *past* sins and their penalty.
            2. In the *present,* it is Jesus who keeps us by His power. I John 1:9 is in the Bible so that we may have daily forgiveness and communion with Him.
            3. In the *future,* it will be Christ who will deliver us from the presence of sin when He takes us to Heaven.
        b. Our salvation is secure because it's based in Christ. Since He cannot fail, neither can the salvation He gives.

    3. Because of His ability to present us faultless before the Father.
        a. Read Hebrews 12:14 and you will find that *"without holiness, no man shall see the Lord."*
        b. Where are we to find this holiness that will enable us to stand before the Lord? Jude 24

and 25 teach us that it is Christ, Himself, who has the ability to present us faultless.

   c.   Without Christ we're not holy; we're only sinners.

      1.   But salvation has placed us "in" Christ. Now we're covered by His righteousness.

      2.   In Him we will be able to stand before the Father holy, and without blemish!

      3.   We can rest assured in our salvation, knowing that it is Christ who keeps us and will someday present us faultless before the Father in Heaven.

SUMMARY: What good is a salvation that doesn't last? What good is salvation unless you can *know* that you've been saved?

God has given us a "know so" salvation. Christians need no longer live with the fear that is connected with the future. They *know* that at the end of this life upon the earth they are going to spend eternity in Heaven. They don't possess this knowledge because they go to church, pray, or give money to the Lord's work, but because they have been saved by the grace of a loving God. They know that His grace saved them. It's the same grace that will keep them saved until they stand before Him someday in Heaven.

If there were no other reasons or evidences to be found, we could stand assured upon I John 5:13: *"These things have I written unto you that believe on the name of the Son of God; that ye may know that ye have eternal life..."*

God has written to us so we will have full assurance of our salvation. He wants us to have this wonderful assurance so we can live with the peace of God in our lives. Don't allow doubts to rob you of the joy of salvation. If Jesus has saved you, your salvation will never fail, for...JESUS NEVER FAILS!

REFLECTIONS: Answer the following questions individually or in class. Give careful attention to your answers. This exercise is what the Bible refers to as *meditation.* Think on these things....

1. Why is having the assurance of our salvation so vital?

    _____

    _____

2. What produces the change in one's life at salvation? What kind of things can we expect to change? How is this an indicator that one has truly been saved?

    _____

    _____

3. What is faith? What part does it play in having the assurance that we've been saved?

    _____

    _____

4. Name at least two ways the Holy Spirit endeavors to help us
   with our assurance of salvation.

   _____

   _____

5. What does I John 2:3-5 teach concerning our salvation and our
   desire to please the Lord? How is this an evidence to help lead
   us to the assurance of our salvation?

   _____

   _____

6. What is chastening? How does this principle relate to the topic
   of this lesson?

   _____

   _____

7. List three or four facts about the change in the life of the jailer
   at Philippi after he was converted. How long did it take for his
   attitudes and actions to change? (The story is found in Acts
   16.)

   _____

   _____

8. If the Bible says in Colossians 2:10 that we are "complete" in
   Christ, what part must we add to our own salvation?

   _____

   _____

9. What is essential before one can stand before God? Why?
   (Hint: Hebrews 12:14 and Revelation 21:27)

   _____

   _____

10. Read Isaiah 61:10 and list what this wonderful verse says to
    you. What are the "garments of salvation"?

    _____

    _____

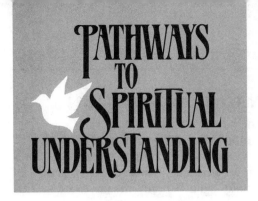

The Carnal Christian and the Spiritual Christian

MAIN SCRIPTURES:
I CORINTHIANS 3:1-23

LESSON AIM: To lead to the understanding that some saved people don't always act Christian in their attitudes and in their actions because they are *carnal,* and have stopped growing in their faith. To show the difference in the life of a *consecrated* Christian and a *carnal* Christian.

SUGGESTED MEMORY VERSES:
I Corinthians 3:1; I Corinthians 3:16; Romans 8:6; and Romans 8:7.

OVERVIEW:

I. WHAT DOES IT MEAN TO BE A CHRISTIAN?

II. THE TWO TYPES OF CHRISTIANS

III. THE BIBLE'S PERFECT EXAMPLE OF A CARNAL CHRISTIAN

IV. THE DIFFERENCE BETWEEN THE CARNAL CHRISTIAN AND THE SPIRITUAL CHRISTIAN

INTRODUCTION: As you read the main text for this lesson, you'll see that the Apostle Paul is writing to the Church members at Corinth. There was trouble in this crowd. Their church was filled with envy, strife and division. Yet in I Corinthians 3:1 Paul calls them brethren. That lets us know that they truly had been saved.

Their problem wasn't that they weren't converted, their problem was one of carnality. They were spiritually immature and had stopped living to please the Lord. Paul said they were "babes in Christ," meaning they hadn't grown at all since they'd been saved. This carnal life was marked by things like jealousy, arguments, fighting and even bragging about who was the most spiritual in the bunch.

It is possible to be a child of God and to come to the point where you stop walking in the *Spirit* and start walking in the *flesh.* When a Christian does this, he will become carnal. A carnal Christian will always be a miserable Christian. Therefore, it's important to learn to guard against that which will cause us to become carnal and lose the blessing of God upon our lives.

We're each responsible for our own growth as a Christian. We must grow above the necessity to be bottle-fed by others, and learn to feed upon the *meat* of God's Word that will build us up and cause us to grow to full stature and maturity. This is God's desire for all of His children.

(Where lines are provided after a Scripture reference, look up the verse and write a one sentence summary of what is Scripture is saying to you.)

I.   WHAT DOES IT MEAN TO BE A CHRISTIAN?

A.   Basic to the study of the carnal Christian versus the spiritual Christian is the proper understanding of what a Christian really is! A previous study covered the Bible's teaching on salvation in great detail. However, there are some additional facts about what it really means to be a Christian.

1.   To be a Christian is to know that you've been saved by God's grace.

a.   There's great misunderstanding today about what it takes to be a Christian. Many think you simply join the church, or are baptized to become a Christian. But make no mistake. No one can lay claim to the name *Christian,* without first being born again.

b.   Perhaps we aren't preaching and teaching God's plan of salvation in its simplicity and truth.

c.   Jesus didn't complicate salvation. He said it required only a childlike faith to be saved. (Matthew 18:3) _____

_____

_____

d.   So, to be a Christian, one ***must*** first be saved. (If you have personal doubts about your own salvation, it would be wise to turn back to lesson 2 the New Birth, and read it carefully until you fully understand how you can be born again and have that assurance in your heart.)

B.   Salvation isn't all that's required to qualify to use the name *Christian.*

1.   By now you understand that one can be saved, yet not living a lot like Jesus did. This was the basic problem at Corinth. They were saved, but not living very Christ-like lives.

To be a Christian actually means to be like Christ in the two primary areas of life. I Corinthians 6:19-20 _____

_____

_____

These verses teach us that we're to bring glory to God in our body (our actions) and in our spirit (our attitudes).

a.   A Christian, then, will endeavor to be Christ-like in ***attitudes.***

To be a Christian is to have Christ-like thoughts and feelings toward others and to allow the Holy Spirit to control your temperament (moods).

b.   To be a Christian is also to be like Christ in

actions. To glorify God in your body, you should endeavor to follow the example of Jesus. The daily life (outward actions) of a Christian is the only "Bible" many people will ever see.

C. A true Christian is also one who lets Christ Jesus be Lord of his life.

1. Since Jesus lived with one great purpose—to do His Father's will—it would be fair to say that this should also be the goal and purpose of the life of every one who claims to be a Christian.
    a. Read Philippians 2:5-8. Write a brief summary of what this passage teaches about Jesus. _____

    _____

    _____

    b. Far too many lives are Christian only in name and not in practice.
    c. If the *secular* rules over the *spiritual* in your life, then Christ isn't Lord!
    d. When one has Christ as the Lord, things like sports, job, housework, gardening and hobbies won't be more important than things like church, prayer, Bible study, Christian fellowship and service to the Lord through the local church.
    e. You'll find that when you allow Jesus to be the Lord of your life He doesn't take away from the enjoyment of life; He adds to it. Those things which you've always enjoyed, if put into their proper place, will be even more enjoyable with the Lord's blessing upon them.

2. The Christian life is an active life. It's a life of doing, going, witnessing, giving, sharing, helping and serving.

3. The Christian life is the abundant life.
    a. It's the best life, and it's the blessed life! It's the life of joy, peace and blessing when Jesus is Lord!
    b. Think about this. If you were placed in a courtroom and accused of being a Christian, would there be enough evidence to convict you?

II. THE TWO TYPES OF CHRISTIANS

A. A Christian is one who not only has been saved, but one who also endeavors to live a Christ-like life in attitudes and actions.
    The Bible teaches us that there are two types of Christians.

1. There is the *carnal* Christian.
    a. The word *carnal* means to be fleshly, or to

care more for the things of the flesh. (Romans 8:5) _____

_____

_____

    b.   Living "in the flesh" (living to care only about material and physical things) doesn't please God.

  2. There is the *spiritual* Christian.
    a.   The word *spiritual* means to care for things in the spiritual realm and to seek those things with greater desire than we seek temporal things. (Romans 13:14) _____

_____

_____

    b.   Galatians 5:16 teaches us that if we will walk in the Spirit we won't be troubled by the flesh.

B.   Whether you'll be a carnal Christian or a spiritual Christian depends largely upon you and your efforts and ambitions.
    a.   Galatians 5:25-26 _____

_____

_____

    b.   What does "walk in the Spirit" mean to you? ___

_____

_____

III. THE BIBLE'S PERFECT EXAMPLE OF A CARNAL CHRISTIAN

A.   The perfect example of a carnal Christian is found in the story of the prodigal son (Luke 15:11-32).

  1. Notice in verse 11 that Jesus said, *"A certain man had **two** sons..."* If He had intended that we only learn the lessons of the prodigal son, He would have just mentioned one son in His story.

  2. The lessons of the prodigal are important and easy to pick out of the story. We learn of the danger of a materialistic heart, the short-lived folly of sin, the end of the backslider's road, the steps of restoration and the wonderful attitude of the father toward a repentant son.

B.   There's another character to be found in Luke 15. He's the elder brother.
    The elder brother is the perfect example of a carnal Christian. Who is he and what does he have to teach us?

  1. He's called a "son" in verse 25, so we know he represents those who are saved.
    a.   By salvation we become the sons of God.
    b.   John 1:12 _____

_____

_____

2.   In verse 29 we learn that he is a servant.
     a.   He, unlike his dropout brother, was still at
          home and still serving his father.
     b.   Even so, there are indicators that let us know
          that he was a carnal son.

3.   He was filled with the spirit of envy and jealousy
     toward his brother.
     a.   See Luke 15:25-28. His anger was generated by
          the special treatment his brother was
          receiving.
     b.   When he should have rejoiced on behalf of his
          brother, he was jealous and envious.
     c.   Envy, then, is an indicator of a carnal life.
          Proverb 27:4 _____

     _____

     _____

4.   His feelings were easily injured, and his wrong
     attitude hindered his fellowship with others.
     a.   Notice his childish attitude, which comes
          across in Luke 15:28.
     b.   He wouldn't go into the house to fellowship
          with the others who had gathered to rejoice
          because his feelings were hurt.
     c.   Being easily offended is a mark of the carnal
          life, and an indicator that one isn't spending
          much time in the Bible. Psalm 119:165 _____

     _____

     _____

5.   He viewed his work for his father as something to
     be endured, rather than something he enjoyed.
     a.   Look at Luke 15:28-29. He is saying, "I've
          'slaved' away my life for you all these years."
     b.   This is one of our big problems today in the
          Lord's work. We serve the Lord, but we don't
          serve Him with the joy we ought to be
          experiencing.
     c.   When serving the Lord has become more
          burden than blessing, it's most likely an
          indicator that you aren't walking in the Spirit
          and may be in danger of becoming a carnal
          Christian.

6.   He was a man who was dominated by **self**.
     a.   Look at Luke 15:29 and count how many times
          he uses words like, "I," "me," and "my."
     b.   He was self-righteous.
     c.   He was self-centered.
     d.   He was filled with self-pity.

e.   When you see these attitudes in yourself, you need to take caution. It's an indicator of one who has become carnal.

7.   He was a complainer who was judgmental and critical of his own brother.
   a.   In Luke 15:30 we see how he complained about the treatment and attention his brother was getting.
   b.   We see railing criticism of his brother.
   c.   He ignored the fact that his brother had repented and come home; he magnified the sins of his brother.
   d.   While it's right that we preach against that which threatens the work of the Lord and tears down and destroys the Word of God, it's wrong to fall into the habit of criticizing others. Romans 14:10-13 _____

   _____

   _____

Criticism is "of the flesh." It endeavors to make one appear spiritual and righteous at the expense of another. This, too, is an indicator of the carnal life.

8.   He didn't share the same concern for the one who had been lost as did his father.
   a.   Notice the father's attitude over one who "was lost and is found" in verse 24. His was the attitude of joy and rejoicing!
   b.   From verse 28 through verse 32 we see the lack of compassion and concern evidenced in the life of the elder brother.
      Truly, the elder brother is a great example of those who are "sons of God" but still walk in the flesh and live a carnal life.

IV. THE DIFFERENCE BETWEEN THE CARNAL AND THE SPIRITUAL CHRISTIAN

A.   There is a difference in their *motives*.

   1.   The carnal Christian lives for the flesh and the desires of the flesh. Romans 8:5 _____

   _____

   _____

   2.   The spiritual Christian lives for the Lord and desires to serve and please Him. II Timothy 2:4 _____

   _____

   _____

B.   There is a difference in their *food*.

   1.   The carnal Christian is still a spiritual baby and feeds only upon the "milk" of God's Word.
      a.   I Corinthians 3:2 _____

_____

_____

b.   Hebrews 5:13-14 _____

_____

_____

2.   The spiritual Christian loves the Word of God in it's entirety, which includes the study of doctrine.
   a.   I Timothy 4:15-16 _____

_____

_____

b.   II Timothy 3:16-17 _____

_____

_____

C.   There is a difference in their **growth**.

1.   The carnal Christian is an infant. He will show the characteristics of immaturity (selfishness, self-centeredness and becoming easily upset with others). I Corinthians 3:1 _____

_____

_____

2.   The spiritual Christian will continue to grow and mature in the faith. (II Peter 3:18) _____

_____

_____

D.   There is a difference in their **walk**.

1.   The carnal Christian walks in instability. (An infant is unstable and depends upon others to help him walk; so does the carnal Christian.) James 1:8 _____

_____

_____

2.   The spiritual Christian walks in the example that Jesus left for him to follow. (Colossians 2:6) _____

_____

_____

E.   There is a difference in their **fruit**.

1.   The carnal Christian allows the cares of this world to choke out the fruitfulness of his life. Matthew 13:22 _____

_____

_____

2.   The spiritual Christian lives a life of fruitfulness for

the Lord's sake.
  a.   Matthew 13:23 _____

_____

_____

  b.   John 15:5-8 _____

_____

_____

F.   There is a difference in their *joy.*
  1.   The carnal Christian will always suffer a loss of joy.
       Psalm 51:12 _____

_____

_____

  2.   The spiritual Christian will have fullness of joy, even
       in adverse circumstances. Romans 14:17-18 _____

_____

_____

G.   There will be a difference in their *reward.*
  1.   The carnal Christian will have no reward when he
       stands before God. I Corinthians 3:13-15 _____

_____

_____

  2.   The spiritual Christian will receive a reward based
       on his labor for the Lord.
       a.   Read Matthew 6:19-21 _____

_____

       b.   Revelation 22:12 _____

_____

_____

SUMMARY: All who have been saved by the grace of God, through faith in Christ Jesus, will be in Heaven someday. However, not all who are saved really live the Christian life here upon this earth.

To be a Christian means more than being saved. It means to mimic the life of Jesus before the world. It means to endeavor to follow in His steps and to live as he lived. Some will say, "The Lord knows I can't be perfect, like Jesus." That's true, but should that keep us from the goal of striving to be more like Him today than we were yesterday? It's the duty of a child of God to grow in the Christian life and to take on more and more of the characteristics of his Father in Heaven.

One will not grow without a proper diet and some sort of exercise. If we're to grow in the faith, we must feed ourselves daily upon the Word of God. We must, as the Bible instructs, "exercise ourselves unto Godliness," which simply means practice being more like Christ. What kind of Christian will you be—carnal or spiritual? That choice must be determined by each of us at the start of every new day.

REFLECTIONS: Answer the following questions individually or in class. Give careful attention to your answers. This exercise is what the Bible refers to as *meditation*. Think on these things....

1. What does the word *Christian* really mean? When is one eligible to use the term?

   _____

   _____

2. In what two areas of life are we told to glorify God? How can we do this?

   _____

   _____

3. What does it mean to be *carnal* as a Christian?

   _____

   _____

4. List some of the characteristics that will become evident in the life of one who is carnal.

   _____

   _____

5. How can one guard against becoming carnal in the Christian life?

   _____

   _____

6. How should a carnal brother or sister be treated?

   _____

   _____

7. List reasons that prove we are wiser to live the spiritual life as opposed to the carnal life.

   _____

   _____

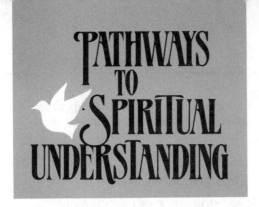

PATHWAYS TO SPIRITUAL UNDERSTANDING

LESSON 5

The Lord's Table and the Purpose of Communion

MAIN SCRIPTURES:
LUKE 22:14-20, and
I CORINTHIANS 11:23-31

LESSON AIM: To help us better understand the meaning behind the ordinance of communion, or the ***Lord's table.*** To lead the Christian to the proper attitude he should have each time he partakes of communion within the local church. To help us see exactly why Jesus began this ordinance and commanded the Church to carry it out until His return.

SUGGESTED MEMORY VERSES:
I Corinthians 11:28; I Corinthians 11:31; I Corinthians 5:7, and I John 1:9

OVERVIEW:

I. THE PERPETUITY OF THE ORDINANCE

II. THE PRINCIPLE ELEMENTS IN THE ORDINANCE

III. THE PRACTICE OF THE ORDINANCE

IV. THE PURPOSE OF THE ORDINANCE

INTRODUCTION: The Lord's table is more than just an ordinance of the Church, more than Christian duty, more than a religious ceremony, and much more than just a portion of a Sunday morning or evening worship service. ***It's a holy time.*** It's a practice Jesus instituted and instructed the Church to continue until He returns and we sit together with Him around His table in His Kingdom. But why? What's the importance and the significance of this ordinance? What was Jesus our Lord trying to impress upon us?

In many cases today, we participate in religious practice without possessing the full understanding of what the Lord intended us to learn. Thus it is with the ordinance of "communion."

In Luke, chapter 22, we find the Lord on His way to Calvary. But before he went to the cross, He paused long enough to share a Passover meal with His disciples. This passover was unlike others they must have shared. This Passover became a new command and created a new ordinance that Christians in all generations would continue.

Today we continue the practice that Jesus Himself began. We mustn't take that lightly. Those who pastor churches must take great care to administer the Lord's table in a way that will please Him. Those who sit together at the Lord's table and share communion must take great care not to miss the intended purposes for gathering together.

Perhaps when you have studied your Bible and prayed over these Bible principles, the Lord's table will take on a wonderful new meaning in your life as a child of God.

(Where lines are provided after a Scripture reference, look up the verse and write a one sentence summary of what this Scripture is saying to you.)

I.   THE PERPETUITY OF THE ORDINANCE

A.   In Luke 22, Jesus began the ordinance of communion.

   1.   How long are we to continue to practice it?
     a.   That answer is found in I Corinthians 11:26.

        _____

        _____

     b.   Note the words, *"till He come."*
     c.   We're to continue to practice this ordinance until the Lord's return.

   2.   How often should we, as a church body, sit together at the Lord's table?
     a.   This question is one that has led to much discussion and to various opinions.
     b.   What does the Bible say?
        1.   Quite honestly, the Bible doesn't make any clear reference as to how frequently the Lord's table (communion) should be observed.
        2.   I Corinthians 11:26 simply states, *"as often as ye eat this bread, and drink this cup...."*
        3.   No set time is given.
        4.   This leaves the freedom of time for communion to be set within each local church.

B.   There is a caution that ought to be observed about communion.

   1.   We ought to be careful that the ordinance of communion doesn't become so customary and usual that we fail to give it proper purpose and understanding.
     a.   Some churches have communion every Lord's Day.
     b.   Some churches have communion once each month on the first or the last Sunday of each month.
     c.   Some churches hold communion every month that has a fifth Sunday.
     d.   Others set this ordinance on a schedule that allows for special observations such as Thanksgiving services, Christmas services or any other special day.

   2.   We should practice this great ordinance without setting our limits upon others when it comes to the matter of when to hold communion.
     If the Word of God doesn't speak on this matter,

we must give one another the liberty to meet together for communion *"as often as ye eat this bread and drink this cup."*

C. We are to continue other things until Jesus returns.

    1. We are to ***preach.***

        a. Jesus preached during His earthly ministry. We must continue this business of preaching, especially in our churches.

        b. The main purpose for preaching is found in I Corinthians 1:21. _____

                _____

                _____

        c. A secondary purpose may be found in II Timothy 4:2. _____

                _____

                _____

        d. List some of the Bible's purposes in preaching.

                _____

                _____

    2. We are to ***pray.***

        a. Luke 18:1 _____

                _____

        b. We are to continue praying until Jesus comes.

    3. We are to ***occupy.***

        a. Luke 19:13 _____

                _____

                _____

        b. To *occupy* is to take possession of enemy territory. We are to stay in this battle with the devil until Jesus returns.

II. THE PRINCIPLE ELEMENTS USED IN THE COMMAND

A. In Luke 22:14-20, we find the two elements that Jesus used as He instituted the Lord's Supper.

    1. He used bread to represent His body.

        a. Verse 19 _____

                _____

                _____

        b. The bread used in the Passover was always unleavened bread. Leaven, in the Bible, is always a type (or symbol) of sin.

        c. This unleavened bread, then, represented the sinless body of Christ, our Passover Lamb.

    d.   It was not Jesus' intention for us to teach that the bread actually became His flesh, but that the bread is a symbol of His sinless life. He used this to teach an object lesson to His disciples and all generations of Christians to follow.

  2. He used the "fruit of the vine" to represent His blood that was shed for the atonement of sin.

    a.   Verse 20 _____

_____

_____

    b.   The "fruit of the vine" mentioned in Luke 18 and Matthew 26:29 was new wine (freshly pressed juice) and not old, or fermented, wine.

    c.   If great care was taken to remove the leaven from the bread because it represented corruption, then certainly the wine (pressed juice) must have also been free from fermentation—another type of corruption.

    d.   Jesus wasn't teaching that the "fruit of the vine" had actually become His blood, but rather that it was an eternal symbol of His pure blood which was shed for the remission of our sins.

III. THE PRACTICE OF THE COMMAND

    Christ intended for the practice of communion to be carried out by the Church throughout all ages.

    The Church was established by our Lord for two primary reasons: the evangelization of the lost world and the fellowship and edification of Christians.

    Jesus instituted communion and established it's practice in the Church for many reasons.

  A.   It's to be a practice in *evangelism.*

    1.   That is not to imply that communion is part of God's plan for salvation.

    2.   We are to show the unsaved what Christ has done for us.

      a.   I Corinthians 11:26 _____

_____

_____

      b.   Communion is a holy practice that shows forth the Lord's death. It is a lesson to all that Christ died for sin. It then, becomes a practice in evangelism.

  B.   It is a practice in *fellowship.*

    1.   The Lord's table is to be observed in the Church that it might promote unity within the Body. Read I Corinthians 10:16-17.

    2.   Sitting together at the Lord's table is to be a

practice in fellowship one with another. It is a time to cast aside anything that would hinder or destroy the unity within the Body (the Church).

C.   It is to be a practice in *self-judgment.*

This is one of the most necessary practices at the Lord's table. I Corinthians 11:28 _____

_____

_____

Verses 29 and 30 teach us the grave danger of taking this matter lightly.

Verse 31 of I Corinthians 11 teaches the great importance of a regular time of self-judgment.

1.   This is a time to judge our *thoughts.*
     a.   The proper place to begin the matter of self-judgment is within our hearts.

     b.   II Corinthians 10:5 _____

     _____

     _____

     c.   Eventually, what we harbor in our hearts will find its way out in our words and our deeds.
     d.   We need to learn how to bring our thoughts into captivity.

2.   It's a time to judge our *words.*
     a.   It's a time to pray the prayer of David found in Psalm 19:14 _____

     _____

     _____

     b.   The words we speak have great ability to bless or to destroy.
     c.   Read Proverb 12:25, Proverb 15:23, and Proverb 18:8.
     d.   Communion is the perfect time to judge our words and confess as sin those which haven't been right and acceptable to God.

3.   It's a time to judge our *attitudes.*
     a.   I Corinthians 6:20 tells us that we're to glorify God in our body (deeds) and in our spirit (our attitudes).
     b.   Attitudes are the "hidden sins" of the heart—things like bitterness, malice, hatred, jealousy, pride, unforgiveness and covetousness.
     c.   At the Lord's table, we should search our hearts and make sure our spirits are sweet and our attitudes bring glory to God.

4.   It's a time to judge our *deeds.*
     a.   We who are saved are the ambassadors of Christ to this world.
     b.   The communion service gives us an

> opportunity to examine our deeds and see if the way we live before others is a good representation of a Christian.

   c.   The Lord's table is a time to examine one's life in every area. As the indwelling Spirit reveals areas where we have sin, we are to confess and forsake those sins so we might be right with God and with others.

   d.   Doing this fulfills the admonition in I Corinthians 11:28 to examine ourselves.

IV. THE PURPOSE OF THIS COMMAND

A.   The purpose of communion is found in Luke 22:19 *"...this do in remembrance of me."*

   1.   The great truth is this: we are far too forgetful, so Christ established this ordinance that in practicing it regularly, we won't forget what He has done. (I Corinthians 11:24 and 25)

   2.   The Jews observed Passover to remind them of the great things God had done on their behalf.
        Passover was especially intended to remind them of their deliverance from the bondage and slavery of Egypt.

   3.   Christ is our Passover Lamb. The Lord's table is our reminder of deliverance from the bondage and slavery of sin. (I Corinthians. 5:7) _____

        _____

        _____

        a.   The Jews had "Passover" to commemorate an *event;*
        b.   We have communion to commemorate a *person.*

B.   What does Christ want us to remember anew each time we sit together at the Lord's table?

   1.   We are to remember *his life* that we might try to live as He lived and follow the example He set for us.

   2.   We are to remember *his death* that we might always be mindful of the cost of our salvation (and that we might remember we are saved by His grace and not our works).

   3.   We are to remember *his resurrection* that we might have full confidence in our faith. (I Corinthians 15:14-22)

   4.   We are to remember *his returning* that we might live in daily readiness and not be ashamed before Him at His coming.

SUMMARY: Over the grave of President John F. Kennedy in Arlington National Cemetery, there burns an eternal flame. That flame burns as a constant memorial to a man who gave his life while serving his nation as president. Its intended purpose is simply to remind. Stroll though any cemetery and you'll find grave markers whose purpose is to remind us of another who is no longer among us here on the earth.

Every year in this country we celebrate a holiday called Memorial Day. Memorial Day is, traditionally, the day we set aside to remember our war dead—those who have given their lives that others may continue to live. It is a good thing to have these reminders because we sometimes tend to be more forgetful than we ought to be. The bottom line is, we need to be reminded.

There is another memorial that we observe in the practice of communion in our churches. It's done to remember our dear Lord and to be reminded of what He has done in our lives. It is also to remind us of the life that He desires us to live as His ambassadors to the world. The life that follows His example best pleases Him. When we stop to remember Him and what He has done, that thought ought to fill us with a great desire to please Him. The next time you sit at the Lord's table, remember it is much more than just a religious ceremony. It is to be a Thanksgiving service, a memorial to Jesus, our living Lord.

REFLECTIONS: Answer the following questions individually or in class. Give careful attention to your answers. This exercise is what the Bible refers to as *meditation.* Think on these things....

1. When was it that Jesus began the ordinance of the Lord's Supper? Out of what Jewish observance was it born?

   _____

   _____

2. When should a church practice communion?

   _____

   _____

3. What was the primary characteristic of the bread that Jesus used? In what way is it a perfect type of His body?

   _____

   _____

4. In what way does the "fruit of the vine" produce types (or symbols) of the blood of Christ? (Think also of the way wine was produced in those days.)

   _____

   _____

5. Christ intended that the ordinance of communion be carried out by the Church through all ages. Who makes up the Church? Who is a proper participant for a communion service?

   _____

   _____

6. Are there times when even a saved person ought not participate in a communion service? If so, when?

    _____

    _____

7. When you read I Corinthians, chapter 11, you come to the conclusion that the Lord's table was being mistreated in the church of Corinth. List your ideas of how this was so.

    _____

    _____

8. What very important principle do we learn from I Corinthians 11:28?

    _____

    _____

9. What is a memorial? Why is the Lord's table a memorial service?

    _____

    _____

10. What do we show forth by fellowshipping together around the Lord's table in our church?

    _____

    _____

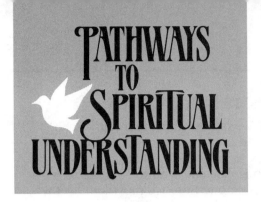

LESSON 6

Baptism

MAIN SCRIPTURES:
MATTHEW 28:18-20; ACTS 2:36-47
ROMANS 6:1-5

LESSON AIM: To lead to a clear Bible-based understanding of the ordinance of baptism. To understand who should be baptized, how baptism is to be conducted, and the whys of baptism.

SUGGESTED MEMORY VERSES:
Matthew 28:19; Acts 2:38; Acts 2:41 and Romans 6:4

OVERVIEW:

I. WHO ARE THE SUBJECTS FOR BAPTISM?

II. WHAT IS THE PURPOSE OF BAPTISM?

III. WHAT IS THE BIBLICAL METHOD OF BAPTISM?

IV. WHY IS BAPTISM IMPORTANT?

INTRODUCTION: They say that people's "last words" are important words. What would be your last statement if you knew you were about to die? Surely one would choose those words with great care. Entire studies have been made of famous last words and their importance.

In Matthew, chapter 28, we find some of the last words of Christ Jesus our Lord before His ascension into Heaven. The statement He made has been called ***The Great Commission.*** Indeed it is! The whole mission of the Church may be found within these few verses of Scripture. We are to go into all the world, preach the Gospel to every person, win others to Christ, baptize our converts, and teach them to observe whatever our Lord has taught us.

Over the years much controversy has arisen over the topic of baptism. In fact, you'll find very little written in theology books or books of doctrine concerning this ordinance. Yet it is a vital part of our Lord's commission to the church. Many of our modern day Church members cannot Scripturally explain baptism to their neighbors. We need to know what the Bible says, and have full assurance of our faith and belief concerning this matter of baptism.

(Where lines are provided after a Scripture reference, look up the verse and write a one sentence summary of what this Scripture is saying to you.)

I.   WHO ARE THE SUBJECTS FOR BAPTISM?

Before we can baptize anyone we must first know who, according to Scripture, should become a candidate for baptism.

Is it our duty to baptize anyone who makes that request? As with any Bible question, we must look to the Bible for our answers.

A.   From the Bible we learn that there are two basic categories of people living on earth.

1.   There are the *saved.*
   a.   A previous lesson discussed the New Birth and how one can be saved. (Refer to lesson number 2.)
   b.   The *saved* are those who, by faith, have trusted Christ as their personal Savior.
   c.   The words saved and born again are synonymous.
   d.   We who are saved, are saved by God's grace and not our merit; therefore, we have nothing about which to boast.

2.   There are the *unsaved.*
   a.   Those who have not yet put their faith and trust in Christ as Savior are unsaved.
   b.   The unsaved aren't unsaved because they're more wicked than those who are saved.
   c.   They're unsaved simply because they haven't been born again.
   d.   All of us are sinners. Some are *saved* sinners, and some are *lost* sinners. The only difference between the two is the blood of Christ!

B.   From these two categories we must make our determination as to who should be baptized.

If you do a "character search" through the Bible, you won't find a single record of anyone ever being baptized until, *first* they were saved. So, we must conclude that salvation is a necessary prerequisite to baptism.

Let's consider a few case studies found in the Bible.

1.   Read Acts 2:36-41. Write verse 41.

_____

_____

   a.   What conclusion do you draw from this story?
_____

   b.   Who was baptized on the day of Pentecost? ___
_____

2.   Read Acts 8:5-12 (the story of Phillip going to Samaria with the Gospel).

     a.   Look at verse 12 _____

     _____   .

     _____

     b.   What conclusion do you draw? _____

     _____

     _____

     c.   What residents of Samaria were baptized? _____

     _____

     _____

3.   Consider the story of Phillip and the Ethiopian eunuch found in Acts 8:26-38.
     a.   Look carefully at verses 35-39.
     b.   What conclusion do you draw? _____

     _____

     _____

     c.   What was Phillip's response to the Ethiopian's question about what would hinder him from being baptized? _____

     _____

     _____

     d.   When did Phillip baptize this man? (Of course, the answer is, after he professed faith in Christ as the only Son of God.)

4.   Let's take our study further into the Book of Acts and look at a story in Acts 10:34-48. This is the story of the Apostle Peter taking this same Gospel message to a Gentile named, Cornelius.
     a.   Pay attention to verse 22 and you'll see that Cornelius was a man who was considered a "good" man by everyone.
     b.   With all his personal goodness he was still lost, and needed Peter to teach him about Christ so that he could be saved.
     c.   Write verse 34 _____

     _____

     _____

     d.   What conclusion do you draw from this story?

     _____

     _____

     _____

     e.   When did Cornelius and the others get baptized? _____

     _____

     _____

5. Look at the story of the man named Crispus, found
    in Acts 18:8.
    a. What kind of man was Crispus? _____

    _____

    _____

    b. Notice carefully the order found in the last
        part of verse 8. _____

    _____

    _____

C. What do we see in common in each of these case
    histories from the Bible?
    1. The 3,000 on the day of Pentecost, the people in
        Samaria, the Ethiopian, Cornelius and his family, and
        Crispus the chief ruler, *all believed, repented
        and were saved before they were baptized.*
    2. Thus, we conclude that the candidate for baptism is
        one who has first believed the Gospel message,
        turned to Christ by faith and has been saved.

II. WHAT IS THE PURPOSE OF BAPTISM?

A. Perhaps it would be better to begin by mentioning what
    baptism doesn't do.

    1. Baptism doesn't take away sin and save.
        a. Titus 3:5 _____

        _____

        _____

        b. Baptism is a *righteous work*. It's something we
            ought to do after we have been saved; but it
            isn't something we do to secure salvation.

    2. Sometimes the language of Acts 2:38 confuses
        people on this matter.
        a. Note the words, *"Repent, and be baptized
            everyone of you in the name of Jesus Christ
            FOR remission of sins...."*
        b. The word "for" in Acts 2:38 in the original
            language is the word *"eis."* It means,
            "because."
        c. Peter isn't teaching that you should be
            baptized to remit sins, rather, *because* your
            sins have been remitted you ought to be
            baptized.
        d. The command to repent precedes the
            command to be baptized. (Repentance brings
            salvation.)

    3. Let's look at a practical illustration from everyday
        life.
        a. "Close the window, it's cold outside" wouldn't
            mean that closing the window makes it cold
            outside, but because it is already cold outside

someone has given the order to close the window.

b.   When Peter said, "Be baptized...for remission of sins," he was saying you need to be baptized because your sins are remitted already!

c.   Don't ever forget that salvation is the gift of God (Romans 6:23). Therefore we cannot earn it by being baptized.

B.   For what purpose, then, are we to be baptized? Romans 6:3 and 4 teach us that baptism sets forth an example of two great Bible truths. Read Romans 6:3-4. Write verse 4.

_____

_____

_____

1.   The death of Christ.
     a.   Christ died for our sins.
     b.   I Corinthians 15:3 _____

     _____

     _____

2.   The resurrection of Christ from the dead!
     (I Corinthians 15:4)
     a.   This doctrine, according to I Corinthians 15:12-23, is the *power* of the Gospel message.
     b.   If Christ be not raised, our faith is in vain.
     c.   I Corinthians 15:17 _____

     _____

     _____

C.   To understand baptism, you must not miss the great truth found in Romans 6:5.

1.   *"For if we have been planted together in the likeness of his death...."*
     a.   The word "likeness" is important. It means "picture."
     b.   Baptism is a likeness, or a picture, of the death, burial and resurrection of Christ Jesus.

2.   What purpose does a picture serve?
     a.   A picture is simply a reminder.
     b.   As a picture is a reminder of another place or another person, baptism is to serve as a reminder to us of the kind of life we're to live while on earth.
     c.   Romans 6:4 says, *"...even so we also should walk in newness of life."*
     d.   As we are **buried** in the likeness of His death, we are **raised** to walk in newness of His life.

3.   Baptism is an outward sign to others of an inward change that has already taken place.
     Baptism is like wearing a wedding ring. One doesn't wear a ring in order to be married, but

because one has already been married and isn't ashamed to show it.

III. WHAT IS THE BIBLICAL METHOD OF BAPTISM?

A.   What does the Bible have to teach us about the method for baptism? Remember, in a question related to the Bible we must seek our answer from the Bible.

   1.   Some sprinkle, some pour, some immerse face forward, some immerse once backward, still others immerse three times backward.
   2.   With all these opinions where is one to find answers?

B.   When considering the question of method, it's vital to remember the fact that baptism, according to Romans 6:5, is to be a likeness of the death, burial and resurrection of Christ Jesus.

   The symbol of a death, burial and resurrection can best be found in baptism by immersion.

   1.   The Greek word for baptize (*baptizo)* means *to dunk* or *to immerse.*
   2.   Two Greek words translated "sprinkle" are *rantizo* and *echeo.* Neither word is found in the Bible in relation to baptism.

C.   Christ set the example in His own baptism.

   1.   Read Matthew 3:13-17 and carefully note the account.
      a.   Matthew 3:16 _____

   _____

   _____

      b.   Notice that Jesus *"went up out of the water,"* leaving little doubt that both He and John had gone down into the water.
      c.   John baptized Jesus in the water. (Keep in mind the meaning of the word *baptizo.)*
      d.   There in the water at His baptism, Jesus portrayed His death, burial and resurrection, thus leaving us His example to follow.

   2.   All other Biblical accounts of baptism follow the same method. See Acts 8:36-39 once again for the story of the baptism of the Ethiopian.

IV. WHY IS BAPTISM IMPORTANT?

At this point some may say, "If baptism doesn't wash away sin and save me, I don't need to be baptized."

What reasons can be given to prove that baptism is an important step in the life of a saved person? Why should you be baptized after you've trusted Christ and been saved?

A.   The only reason that should be needed is the fact that Jesus our Lord commanded baptism to follow repentance and conversion.

   1.   John 15:10 _____

   _____

   _____

   It's difficult to say that we love the Lord if we don't
   keep His commandments.
   2.   Baptism becomes an evidence of our obedience to
        the Lord and our love for the Lord. John 15:14 _____

   _____

   _____

B.   Jesus' command should be all that those who have been
     born again need in order to follow the Lord's example
     and be baptized, but there are other reasons for baptism.
     1.   Baptism identifies us with Christ.
          a.   Galatians 3:27 _____

          _____

          _____

          b.   Read Galatians 3:26. You'll find, once again,
               that we become the children of God by faith;
               but baptism is that which identifies us with
               our Lord.
          c.   Baptism is like the uniform a soldier wears.
               While the uniform doesn't make him a soldier
               (he became a soldier before he was given a
               uniform) that uniform identifies him with his
               country and his leader.

     2.   Baptism is a practice in evangelism in that it is an
          outward evidence to others of our salvation.
          a.   Baptism is a perfect portrayal of the Gospel
               message as outlined in I Corinthians 15:3-4.
          b.   It's the believer's testimony to others of the
               change that has taken place in his life, and of
               his desire to walk in this new life as a child of
               God, pleasing to his heavenly Father.

     3.   Baptism identifies us with, and attaches us to a
          local body of believers (a church).
          a.   Acts 2:41 teaches that on the day of Pentecost
               those who were saved were also that same day
               baptized and ***added to the church.***
          b.   Through baptism we prove our desire to be
               obedient to the Word of God, and, we show
               our desire and need to be enjoined to a local
               body of believers. (We'll study the importance
               of the Church in the life of every saved
               individual in another lesson.)

SUMMARY: With all the difference of opinion that surrounds the
matter of baptism, let us not lose sight of the fact that baptism is
to portray a likeness of the death, burial and resurrection of Jesus.
When we go into the waters of baptism after our salvation we are,

in essence, going into the water to show the desire to "die to self" and "to live for Christ."

Baptism is an important step but, it isn't the first step. The first step is repentance and faith in Christ as Savior. There is no story recorded in the Bible of anyone who was baptized until after they had first believed the Gospel story and had been saved.

Salvation is the first and foremost prerequisite to baptism. Baptism is our evidence to the Lord of our love for Him, and our desire to live in obedience to Him as His child. It's a proof to others that we aren't ashamed to be identified with the One who loved us and gave Himself for us.

If you have been baptized, remember that you were buried in the likeness of His death and raised to walk in the newness of life. Don't just simply "talk" Christ to others; "walk" Christ before others!

REFLECTIONS: Answer the following questions individually or in class. Give careful attention to your answers. This exercise is what the Bible refers to as *meditation*. Think on these things....

1. What elements did Jesus include as part of His great commission to the Church?

   _____

   _____

2. What is the first prerequisite to baptism? List one or two Bible examples.

   _____

   _____

3. What can baptism not do? Why?

   _____

   _____

4. Why do you think confusion and controversy have arisen over baptism?

   _____

   _____

5. According to Romans 6:3-5, what purpose does baptism serve?

   _____

   _____

6. Give your opinion on the method for baptism, and perhaps, the reason (or reasons) there are various methods practiced in different churches.

   _____

   _____

7. Why did Jesus get baptized?

   _____

8. Among the reasons that prove the importance of baptism for one who is saved, in your opinion, what is the greatest?

_____

_____

9. In what way is baptism like a soldier's uniform?

_____

_____

10. In what way can a baptism service serve as an evangelistic endeavor?

_____

_____

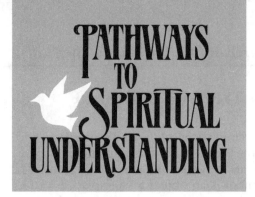

LESSON 7

The Importance of the Church in the Christian's Life

MAIN SCRIPTURES:
MATTHEW 16:13-18; ACTS 2:41-47;
I PETER 2:1-5

LESSON AIM: To show that Jesus established the local church to carry out not only His great commission, but also for the spiritual health of the believer. To show, from the Bible, the importance of faithful attendance to the house of God on the Lord's Day. To show the benefits provided the believer through attachment to a local church.

SUGGESTED MEMORY VERSES:
Hebrews 10:25; Ephesians 3:21; Matthew 16:18

OVERVIEW:

I. THE THREE BIBLICAL TYPES (SYMBOLS) OF THE CHURCH

II. THE SEVEN MARKS OF A SPIRITUAL CHURCH

III. WHAT HAPPENED TO THE MAN WHO STAYED HOME FROM CHURCH?

INTRODUCTION: A barber and his patron were discussing the church attended by the gentleman getting his hair cut. The man in

the chair said to the barber, "I don't intend to ever go back to that church again. Every year we have a big ice cream social in the church hall. And every year the servings get smaller and smaller, and the cost keeps going up. I said if that happened again this year, I wouldn't go back to church again. And I'm not!"

Can it really be that church has become little more than a place for social gatherings? Surely the Lord had more in mind than just ice cream and cake when He told Peter, *"Upon this rock I will build my church; and the gates of hell shall not prevail against it."*

What is the main business of the local church? What benefits can the Christian expect in his or her life from attending church faithfully? Why did the Lord command that we not forsake the attendance of His house (Hebrews 10:25)?

(Where lines are provided after a Scripture reference, look up the verse and write a one sentence summary of what this Scripture is saying to you.)

I. THE THREE BIBLICAL TYPES (SYMBOLS) OF THE CHURCH

The Church is much more than a social club. It's the place where God's people meet together to pray for, plan and carry out the work of God. There are three symbols of the church found in the Bible. Each symbol is an object lesson, placed into the Word of God to teach us some great truth about the ministry, the mission, or the manner of the Church.

A.   In I Corinthians chapter 12, the Church is called a ***body***.

    1.   Read I Corinthians 12:12-27

        a.   Verse 12 _____

        _____

        _____

        b.   Verse 27 _____

        _____

        _____

    2.   There are many things to learn from the symbolism of the Church as a body. One such lesson is that the body must have life or it's powerless and useless.

        a.   A body that's dead (without the spirit living within) serves no use and performs no useful purpose.

        b.   In Revelation 3, God's Word says the church of Sardis had a name that said it lived; yet, it was "dead."

        c.   The key to having a living faith and a lively church is found in Revelation 3:3. _____

        _____

        _____

        We must keep fresh in our minds what the Lord has done for us. A constant mindfulness of His grace and goodness to us will keep life in the body.

    3.   Another lesson found in this symbolism is that a body has organization and structure.

        a.   The human body was designed and built by God. He put the head in the right place, feet in the right place, hands in the right place and every other member of the human body in just the right place.

        b.   I Corinthians 12:18 teaches that the Lord put together the body called the Church.

        c.   In this body (the Church) every member serves a useful purpose for the good of the entire body.

        d.   Colossians 1:18 teaches that Christ is the head of the body called the Church. We're the members of the body, He is the Head.

    4.   From the example of a body, we also learn that

there is perfect unity, care and cooperation among all the members of the body.

   a.   Read I Corinthians 12:20-21 and 25 again.

   b.   This passage clearly states that in the church, all must learn to work together and have the same care one for another.

   c.   Can you imagine the feet going on strike against the rest of the body? Just think of the results.

   d.   Since, in the physical body, each member works in perfect unity with all the others, doesn't it make sense that in the spiritual body (the church) every member should work in unity and harmony with every other member to get the work of God done?

B.   The next symbol of the church is a ***building***.

   1.   In Ephesians 2:19-22, the Church is called a spiritual building.

      a.   Verse 22 _____

      _____

      b.   The church is called the habitation of God. ___

      _____

      _____

   2.   From this symbol we learn the importance of a good foundation. Every secure building *must* have a good foundation upon which it rests.

      a.   The foundation for the Church is (or ought to be) the Word of God.

      b.   According to Acts 20:32, the Word of God is able to build the Christian up and make him strong.

      c.   The foundation for faith, doctrine, preaching, planning and all work must be the Bible.

   3.   Every building must have builders.

      a.   No building is ever raised without the sweat, labor and efforts of builders.

      b.   Read I Corinthians 3:9-10. It says we're to be laborers together in building up the Church.

      c.   Some lay the foundation; others continue to build upon that foundation.

      d.   Are you a "builder" in your church? Do you strive to keep building upon the foundation that others before you have laid?

   4.   Every building has a purpose.

      a.   Every building is built to "do" something and to serve some specific purpose.

      b.   The purpose of the Church is found in Ephesians 3:21 _____

      _____

      _____

   c.   The church is to bring glory to God in all
         ages.
   d.   How can the Church bring glory to God in
         this generation? (John 15:8)

C.   The third symbol of the church is the **bride.**

   1.   Ephesians 5:30-32 likens the Church to the *bride of
         Christ.* Verse 32 _____

         _____

         _____

   2.   Every bride has a specific day when she is joined to
         the groom in marriage.
         a.   No one is born already married. There is a day
               when this commitment is made.
         b.   No one is born into this life already saved and
               joined to the Body of Christ.
         c.   Just as there is a specific wedding day for
               every bride, there is a specific day when one
               is born again into God's family.

   3.   A bride's duty, according to the Bible, is to be
         submissive to her husband.

         a.   Ephesians 5:22-23 teaches this principle. Verse
               24 teaches that the Church is to be submissive
               to Christ.
         b.   As a good husband only seeks the best for his
               bride, so our dear Lord only seeks the best for
               His Church. It is, therefore, rebellion not to be
               submissive to Him in all areas of life.

   4.   A bride is to live a pure life and be faithful to her
         husband.
         a.   God wants a holy Church, a clean church. See
               Ephesians 5:26-27.
         b.   Write I Timothy 4:12 _____

               _____

               _____

         c.   Notice the areas of life in which those who are
               saved are to be an example.
         d.   Christ wants His people to be faithful and to
               live as an example.

II.   THE SEVEN MARKS OF A SPIRITUAL CHURCH

According to the Apostle Peter, in I Peter 2, a church is a
"spiritual house." But what is it that indicates spirituality? Is it
a loud church service filled with sounds of enthusiasm? Is it
using the proper religious language and jargon?

   While it isn't wrong to have enthusiasm in church, these
things alone aren't dependable indicators of a spiritual
church. In fact, no church will be any more spiritual than are
its members. This is the key to the spirituality of any church.
One cannot read Acts 2 without finding a church that was
truly spiritual.

There are seven marks of spirituality found in this chapter of the Bible—seven traits of a truly spiritual church in Jerusalem. As we look at them let us be mindful of the leading of the Holy Spirit as He molds each of us into the kind of church member that can help produce a more spiritual church.

A.   In a spiritual church there will be **prayer.**

1.   The church at Jerusalem was begun after a great time of prayer. Acts 1:14 _____

_____

_____

2.   Read Acts 4:31. Notice that the place was shaken when they prayed, and the result of this prayer was greater boldness to proclaim the message of the Gospel.

3.   The average Christian today spends less than 20 minutes a day in prayer—and hours reading the newspaper and watching television.
   a.   Could this be the reason we lack the power of God in our ministries?
   b.   There would be more power in our Sunday school classrooms, choirs, ministries and pulpits if we who are members of a church would pray more.

B.   In a spiritual church, there will be **unity.**

1.   Read Acts 1:14 again; then read Acts 2:1. Write Acts 2:1. _____

_____

_____

2.   They were found together in one place and in one accord.
   a.   They were unified! There was no division to be found. No "sides' to take, no fusses, no hurt feelings!
   b.   This church meeting was an example of working together in unity.
   c.   The most important ingredient within a church body, other than the power of God, is unity. We cannot have God's power while there is no unity.

3.   Division is one of Satan's most oft-used tools within the church.
   a.   A spiritual church must have spiritual people who will serve together in unity!
   b.   Ephesians 4:3, says to "keep the unity." If we're to do that, we must learn the principle found in Ephesians 4:27. _____

_____

_____

C.   In a spiritual church, there will be *fellowship.*

   1.   Acts 2:42 teaches that the church at Jerusalem
        continued in "fellowship".
           By definition, *fellowship* means: "to share
        interest, feelings and companionship with others."

   2.   To walk in fellowship with others demands an
        agreement upon the essentials of the Christian faith.
        Amos 3:3 _____

        _____

        _____

   3.   Fellowship also means warmth, friendliness and
        concern for one another. Without these three
        Christian graces no church can be truly spiritual.

D.   In a spiritual church, there will be *giving.*

   1.   It's impossible to be spiritual and stingy at the same
        time.
        a.   Acts 2:44-45 teaches us of the great
             willingness of the Christians in the church of
             Jerusalem to give.
        b.   No church will ever grow without a spirit of
             sharing.
        c.   Giving is a matter of the heart, and an
             indicator of our love for others. Therefore, a
             spiritual church is also a giving church.

E.   In a spiritual church, there will be *Bible teaching and
     Bible preaching.*

   1.   One of the best ways to grow in the Spirit is to
        spend time in the Word of God. I Peter 2:2 _____

        _____

        _____

   2.   If we fail to maintain a strong course in this area of
        teaching and preaching the Bible, we will soon have
        churches filled with spiritual babies who haven't
        grown in the Lord.
           Spiritual people are those who enjoy listening to
        the Word of God as it is taught or preached from
        the pulpit.

   3.   Notice again, in Acts 2:41-42, how the Word of God
        was received. Note, in verse 42, how they
        continued in "doctrine."
           Write the results as recorded in Acts 6:7 _____

        _____

        _____

   4.   The Bible hasn't lost it's power to convict, to
        convert and to change lives! A spiritual church will
        be a church where the Word of God has primary
        importance.

F. In a spiritual church, there will be *joy and a gracious testimony.*

Pay close attention to two small, and often overlooked, portions of Scriptures.

1. In Acts 2:46 we read, *"...did eat their meat with gladness and singleness of heart."*
    a. There was joy evident in the lives of these people.
    b. When visitors enter the doors of your church on any given Sunday, do they find people who show the joy of the Lord by the way they look and by the way they walk and talk?

2. In verse 47, note these two words, *"...having favor."*
    a. They had a gracious testimony which was attractive to others.
    b. One minister used to say, "Build a fire in your church and people will come to get warm."
    c. In this cold world, may God help each of us add to the warmth and the testimony of our church, so others will have a desire to come in and be warmed.

G. In a spiritual church there will be *evangelism.*

1. Don't overlook Acts 2:47. It ends with the words, *"And the Lord added to the church daily such as should be saved."*

2. As these Church members went out to the surrounding areas and into the market places, they did their best to tell others what Christ had done for them.
    a. The very best advertisment is by "word of mouth." As they spread the Word, God blessed daily, with people being saved and added to the church.
    b. Think of the great potential for church growth if each member determines to find just one person in need of the Savior each year and bring him in. What growth that would be!
    c. Spiritual members make a spiritual church.

III. WHAT HAPPENED TO THE MAN WHO STAYED HOME FROM CHURCH?

Why is church attendance so important in the life of a believer? What does one miss by not being in church on Sunday?

A wonderful Bible story about a disciple named Thomas best illustrates what one misses by skipping church. In John 20:19-31 you will find the story about the time Jesus met with His disciples just after His resurrection. Verse 19 tells us it was the "first day of the week," and the disciples were assembled together. This would, of course, be Sunday evening when God's people had joined together for a meeting. What a good example of what takes place in our churches every

Sunday. Verse 24 lets us know that Thomas was not with them on the Sunday night when Jesus came. What did he miss by not being in church on Sunday night?

A.   He missed out on the fellowship with other believers.

    1.   Christian fellowship is vital to the spiritual health of any saved person.

        a.   By skipping church you miss this great source of strength for your life.

        b.   According to I John 3:14, a love for the brethren (other believers) is an evidence of salvation.

    2.   The Christian life consists of three things:

        a.   Worship

        b.   Stewardship

        c.   Fellowship

B.   He missed the Lord's blessing that all the others received.

    1.   In John 20:19 we see that Jesus pronounced *"Peace be unto you."*

        a.   A good church helps keep the "peace of God" in the Christians heart and in his home.

        b.   It's when one separates himself from other believers that he makes himself an isolated target for the devil.

    2.   Verse 20 _____

        _____

        _____

        a.   The disciples were glad.

        b.   Thomas missed the joy shared by those who were present that night.

        c.   Great numbers of Christians lose the "joy of the Lord" in their lives after skipping church for an extended period of time.

C.   Thomas missed the Lord's great commission and command to His disciples.

    1.   Verse 21 _____

        _____

        _____

        a.   Jesus made clear His plan to send believers out to preach the gospel so that others may hear and be saved.

        b.   Thomas missed hearing what God wanted him to do that night by not being present.

        c.   Perhaps this is why we hear nothing more of Thomas in the Scriptures after this event.

    2.   Church is the place where the "man of God" (pastor) brings a message from the Word of God in order that the Christian may know what God wants him to do. Just think what is being missed by those who miss church!

D. Thomas missed the filling of the Holy Spirit.
  1. Verse 22 _____
    _____
    _____

    a. The filling of the Holy Spirit is reserved for the obedient Christian. (We will study this in a future lesson.)
    b. We need God's power to do His work effectively. This was why the filling of the Holy Spirit was so necessary for these men. (And for Christians today!)

E. By missing this meeting, Thomas became a doubter.
  One of the fastest ways for the Christian's faith to decline is to fall into the habit of skipping church.

    a. Romans 10:17 _____
      _____
      _____

    b. Faith increases in relation to the amount of time spent either reading the Bible or listening to the Bible as it is taught or preached.

F. By missing this meeting with the others, Thomas was ashamed and embarrassed when the Lord returned.
  Read verses 27 through 29 again, and you cannot help but feel the shame of Thomas as he stood before the Lord.
  How many Christians would be ashamed if Jesus returned again on a Sunday?

SUMMARY: Never underestimate the importance of church in the life of a Christian. A church is like a fireplace in some ways. When you reach into a fireplace with a poker and remove a live coal, that coal will, little by little, lose it's light and warmth until it ceases to burn at all. It is, for all intents and purposes, a dead coal. It radiates no light and no heat. However, if you place that same coal back into the fireplace it won't be long until it begins to glow once again.

That's exactly why the devil endeavors to get God's people out of church. The church is the source of light and warmth for our lives. Together we can make the light burn brighter, and together we can spread warmth where hearts are cold.

If Jesus loved the church enough to die for it, as we learn from reading Ephesians chapter five, then you and I ought to love it enough to live for it! You need your church. It will be a blessing in your life and a place where you can grow in the grace and knowledge of your Savior. Your church also needs you. There is strength in unity and in numbers. Endeavor to become a church member whose light shines and whose heart is warm.

REFLECTIONS: Answer the following questions individually or in class. Give careful attention to your answers. This exercise is what the Bible refers to as *meditation*. Think on these things....

1. Why is the church likened to a body in I Corinthians, chapter 12?

   _____

   _____

2. Who is to be the head of this body? What function does the head serve?

   _____

   _____

3. What are the other two symbols of the church used in Scripture? List at least one characteristic of each symbol and how it relates to the Church.

   _____

   _____

4. List the seven marks of a spiritual church in the priority you think they should take. Why did you list your first choice as the number one priority?

   _____

   _____

5. Is the Church only a building? Why?

   _____

   _____

6. What is the main business of the Church in the world today?

   _____

   _____

7. List some of the things one misses by not belonging to, or not attending church faithfully.

   _____

   _____

8. In your opinion, what are the elements found in a growing church?

   _____

   _____

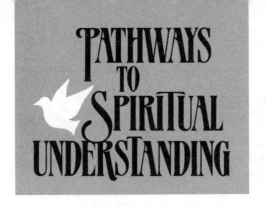

LESSON 8

Prayer

MAIN SCRIPTURES:
DANIEL 10:1-14; MATTHEW 6:1-7;
JAMES 5:13-18

LESSON AIM: To learn, from the Bible, how to pray effectively. To understand what it is that hinders prayers, and to learn how to avoid such things.

SUGGESTED MEMORY VERSES: John 15:7; James 4:3; Proverbs 8:9; Psalm 66:18; Matthew 7:7

OVERVIEW:

   I. LESSONS ON PRAYER FROM AN OLD TESTAMENT CHARACTER

  II. OTHER REASONS FOR UNANSWERED PRAYER

 III. WHAT CAN EFFECTIVE PRAYER ACCOMPLISH?

 IV. THE SECRET TO A SUCCESSFUL PRAYER LIFE

INTRODUCTION: The main characters in a popular weekly TV series found themselves in a terrible predicament. Doom was about to

befall them at any minute. They tried everything they knew to get out of trouble but still failed. Finally, one man turned to the other and asked, "Well, what do we do now?" To this question the other character replied, "If you think it will do any good, we could pray."

That's a pretty sad attitude, yet many saved people today do just that. They try everything else first. Then, in desperation, they finally decide to pray. It seems that which ought to be first (prayer) is that which often becomes a last resort. How we need to learn to pray effectively! This lesson will explore examples of prayer from the Bible. Our goal will be to learn how to get our prayers answered, and what the cause may be when they are not.

(Where lines are provided after a Scripture reference, look up the verse and write a one sentence summary of what this Scripture is saying to you.)

I.   LESSONS ON PRAYER FROM AN OLD TESTAMENT CHARACTER

Daniel was a man of prayer. That pretty well sums up his life. Yet even Daniel experienced what seemed to be a delay in receiving an answer to a very specific prayer to God.

Everyone who has ever spent much time in prayer has had this experience. What can we learn from Daniel and his prayer life that will help us be more effective when we pray? Read Daniel 6:4-11 and Daniel 10:1-14.

A.   Daniel was faithful and regular in his prayer time.

Daniel 6:10 teaches us that Daniel had a "custom" that included regular prayer.

1.   How often did Daniel pray, according to this passage of Scripture?

2.   Perhaps it would be helpful to our prayer life if we set a time and made it our custom to pray.

B.   Daniel was persistent in his prayers.

In Daniel, 6:7 we learn that the King passed a decree that made it illegal to pray for 30 days.

1.   What did Daniel do? Verse 10 _____

_____

_____

2.   Even fear of the den of lions could not keep Daniel from praying.

C.   Daniel trusted God in his prayers.

He was willing to go into the lion's den trusting God to help him and protect him.

1.   Note Daniel 6:23. List the reason that no manner of hurt came upon Daniel. _____

_____

_____

2.   Faith and trust in God are necessary ingredients in effective prayer.

D.   Daniel learned the reason for the delay in his answer from God.

1.   The reason is found in Daniel 10:12-14.
    a.   There was a spiritual battle taking place between the *angels of light* and the *angels of darkness* over Daniel's prayer.
    b.   Satan is a very real enemy to the people of God. He is called the god of this world in II Corinthians 4:4.

2.   If we could lift the veil that stands between the *physical* world and the *spiritual* world, we would realize that a very real spiritual battle goes on all around us.
    a.   We ought to thank God for His divine

protection and watch-care over His own!

  b.   Psalm 34:7 _____

  _____

  _____

  c.   According to Hebrews 12:22 this company of
        angels is innumerable.

  May God help us to never give up on our prayers, no
matter how long the silence from God may seem when
we are seeking an answer. Prayer is heard in Heaven. In
many cases the answer may already be on it's way. Just
keep praying!

II.   OTHER REASONS FOR UNANSWERED PRAYER.

  This "spiritual" battle isn't the only reason prayers are
hindered. Sometimes (and perhaps most often) the problem
lies not in the fault of others, but within ourselves. The Word
of God lists numerous things as hinderances to prayers. These
cause us to become ineffective when we pray. What are some
of these hinderances?

A.   God isn't obligated to answer the prayers of the unsaved.

  1.   This Bible truth is often misunderstood, but
        nevertheless, Scripturally true.
        a.   Proverb 15:29 _____

        _____

        _____

        b.   John 9:31 _____

        _____

        _____

  2.   As a father is only obligated to his own child, thus
        it is with God.
        a.   Read John 10:14 and 26-27.
        b.   Far too many people believe they can call on
              the name of God on Sunday, take His name in
              vain on Monday, and still get an answer to
              their prayers.
        c.   Salvation is a prerequisite to an effective
              prayer life.

B.   A doubtful attitude hinders prayers.

  1.   Read James 1:6-7. Write the reason this passage
        gives for unanswered prayer.
        a.   _____

        _____

        b.   Remember Daniel and the way he trusted God.

C.   Selfish motives or desires hinder prayers.

  1.   James 4:3 _____

_____

_____

2. How many times do our prayers sound like a "want list" from God?

3. Job 35:13 says, *"Surely God will not hear vanity, neither will the Almighty regard it."*

4. God doesn't answer vain requests. If this is your problem, you need to adjust your attitude towards the things you're seeking from God. Then pray again.

5. Learn to pray as Jesus prayed by ending with, *"not my will Lord, but thine be done."*

D. Impatience will hinder your prayer life.

1. Daniel prayed on one occasion for three full weeks and yet continued to trust God for an answer.

2. Read Hebrews 11:6 and you'll see that God is the rewarder of those who diligently seek Him.

3. Write Psalm 40:1. _____

_____

_____

E. Neglecting to spend time in the Bible will hinder your prayers.

1. John 15:7 _____

_____

_____

There's no way the words of Jesus can abide in you unless you spend time in the Word of God.

2. I John 3:22
   a. We receive of Him *because* we keep His commandments. You cannot know His commandments without reading and studying His Word.
   b. Proverbs 28:9 _____

_____

_____

F. An unforgiving attitude will hinder your prayers.

1. We live in an imperfect world filled with imperfect people. Sooner or later, someone will offend you.
   a. If you harbor this offence in your heart you will hinder your prayers.
   b. Read Mark 11:25-26. List the lessons you learn from this important passage. _____

_____

_____

2. We must learn to live according to Colossians 3:13
    if we want to be effective when we pray.

G. Disharmony at home will hinder one's prayer life.

When the harmony and the unity between a husband
and wife is broken through strife, neither person will be
effective in prayer. (I Peter 3:7-8) _____

_____

_____

H. Harboring unconfessed sin will keep prayer from being
    answered.

1. The Bible could be no clearer on this subject than
    it is in Psalm 66:18. _____

_____

_____

2. I Peter 3:12 offers further proof.
    a. To whom does the Lord open His ears? _____

_____

_____

    b. Whom is the face of the Lord against? _____

_____

_____

3. According to Isaiah 59:2, sin separates us from God.
    During this separation, our prayers are hindered
    because of our unconfessed sin.

4. It is important to include a time of heart searching
    when we come to the Lord in a time of prayer;
    confess any sin the Holy Spirit brings to mind.
        Psalm 139:23-24 is a good prayer to offer to the
    Lord each time we approach him in private prayer.

III. WHAT CAN EFFECTIVE PRAYER ACCOMPLISH?

In the Book of James, chapter five, we find a great principle
about prayer. In verse 17 we meet a man named Elijah whose
prayers stopped the heavens from giving rain. When, three
and one-half years later, he prayed for rain, it came in
response to his request. What a prayer life Elijah had! Yet the
Bible is very careful to tell us in verse 17 that Elijah was a
man *"subject to like passions as we are."*

That means he was made of the same stock as you and I.
He didn't have the "market cornered" in heaven; he just
learned how to pray effectively. What can we expect to see
from our prayers? What can prayer accomplish?

A. Eternal Life is secured through prayer.

1. People today go to great lengths trying to secure
    heaven for themselves through good works when
    all they really need is to repent (turn from sin) and
    call on the name of the Lord through prayer.

2. Romans 10:10 teaches us, *"with the heart man believeth unto righteousness; and with the mouth confession is made unto salvation."*
   a. Romans 10:13 _____

   _____

   _____

   Notice: *"for whosoever shall call...."*
   b. This is the first and most important prayer that one must pray.

B. Broken fellowship with God many be restored through prayer.

1. It's possible for the Christian to lose the closeness of fellowship with God.
   a. This usually happens slowly, over a period of time.
   b. It happens as we spend less and less time with the Lord in Bible reading and in prayer.
   c. Little by little, sin creeps into our lives until one day we feel far from God. If you feel far from God, be assured *He* has not moved. It is our obligation to come back to Him.

2. How do we come back to God once close fellowship has been broken?
   a. God awaits just a ***prayer*** away from His children.
   b. I John 1:9 _____

   _____

   _____

3. If we confess (pray), what does He do?
   a. King David is a classic example of one who lost the joy of his salvation and wandered far from God.
   b. Read Psalm 51:1-12. Prayer restored David to his place of fellowship with God.

C. Infirmities may be healed in response to faithful prayer.

Study this Bible principle very carefully.

1. It is not always God's will to heal us from every infirmity. If it were, we would never die, for it is always some physical infirmity that claims our life in the final analysis. The body wears out. From the moment of birth it is on its march to the grave.
   a. In many instances in the Bible, God used sickness and even death so that He might receive glory. We ought, therefore, to be willing to bear out infirmity if God is going to be glorified.

2. Sometimes it is God's will to heal an infirmity, but we simply don't ask in prayer (James 5:13-16).
   The Lord has given us good doctors and modern

technology. Often, however, He is just waiting to answer a prayer about sickness, but we don't ask Him.

3. In II Kings 20:1-5 you can read the story of King Hezekiah, who was warned that he was going to die of his sickness. What did he do? He prayed! What was the result? _____

_____

_____

    a. James 5:15 says it is the prayer of faith that brings healing. That is, healing is dependent upon the faith of the one praying.

    b. We must learn to pray in faith not only for ourselves, but for others who stand in need of prayer.

D. Deliverance from trouble may be found through prayer.

1. Trouble is one thing that is common to all men. We all will have our personal share of troubles in this life. But we do not all handle our troubles in the same manner.

2. When troubles or difficulties come to some they struggle, plot, scheme and even lose sleep. Then, perhaps as a last resort, they will pray.

3. Prayer ought to top our list of things to do when we face troubles!

    a. In many parts of our nation, a telephone number has been established to bring help quickly to those who are in trouble.

    b. For the Christian, Psalm 50:15 is as good as dialing 911. _____

_____

_____

4. There is a great host of unseen agents just waiting to help God's children when in trouble or facing difficulty.

    Read the story of Elisha's servant found in II Kings 6:13-17 for a great Bible story proving God's ability to protect.

E. Material needs can be supplied through prayer.

1. God never has a recession. His bank is never in danger of going broke. God is able to meet and supply all our needs through prayer.

2. God has obligated Himself to do so through the Bible.

    a. Philippians 4:6 tells us not to be anxious (worried) about our needs.

    b. Philippians 4:19 is God's promise of supply. ___

_____

_____

_____

   c.   Even in our Lord's model prayer, He taught us to pray for our daily bread (our daily needs).

F.   Revival comes in answer to sincere prayer.

   1.   We often talk in our churches about the need for revival. But how does revival come?
       a.   Can an evangelist "preach in" a revival?
       b.   Can we advertise and fill the churches with people to bring about revival?

   2.   God's formula for revival involves prayer. Chronicles 7:14 _____

_____

_____

     Notice the importance of prayer in seeking a time of revival.

G.   There are many more things that prayer can do in our lives. Take your Bible and a concordance and look up verses on prayer. You'll soon see what prayer can do. We can sum it up in Jeremiah 33:3 _____

_____

_____

IV. THE SECRET TO A SUCCESSFUL PRAYER LIFE

It has been said, "The secret to prayer is prayer in secret." This is very true. If we want to learn to pray effectively we need to learn to pray in secret. The disciples asked the Lord to teach them how to pray (Luke 11:1). Prayer must be something we can learn to do better. In Matthew 5:5-15, Jesus taught us how to pray.

A.   The **_people_** of prayer.

     Matthew 6:6 says, _"But thou...."_

   1.   Prayer isn't something we should ask others to do for us until we have prayed personally.

   2.   Jesus didn't say, "But when your pastor prays...." He said when _you_ pray.

   3.   You need to take personal inventory of your prayer life today.

B.   The **_period_** of prayer.

     Matthew 6:6 continues, _"...when thou prayest...."_

   1.   You need to pray, and if you are going to pray, you need to have a regular time set aside that you give to prayer.

   2.   Daniel's custom was to pray three times every day. That means he had a habit of praying at regular times.

3. We set a time to work, to eat, to play and to sleep. We ought also to set a time for prayer.

4. Many people set aside time for prayer during the first part of the day.

5. Psalm 63:1 _____

_____

_____

C. The *place* of prayer.

As we continue reading Matthew 6:6 the Bible says, *"...enter into thy closet...."*

1. Do you have a place where you go to spend time in prayer?

2. To be effective in our praying, we need a place set apart from all distractions.
   a. Elijah prayed on top of Mt. Carmel,
   b. Daniel prayed before his window.
   c. Jonah prayed from a whale's belly.
   d. Paul prayed in prison.
   e. The early church prayed in the upper room.
   f. Jesus prayed in the mountains. Luke 6:12 _____

   _____

   _____

   g. We all ought to set aside a place where we can be alone with the Lord and pray.

D. The *privacy* of prayer.

"...and when thou hast shut thy door...."

1. The place of prayer needs to be a place of privacy.

2. The reason for this is found in verse 5. When we pray in a public place, we often pray to please the crowd around us rather than to get God's attention.

3. When we are alone with the Lord we can be perfectly honest in our time of prayer.

E. The *privilege* of prayer.

Verse 6 teaches us that we have a Father in Heaven who will hear our prayers.

1. What a great privilege it is to be able to come to God's throne through prayer and receive an audience with Him!

2. We ought not take the privilege lightly.

3. Through prayer we come into the presence of the King of kings and the Lord of lords.

F. The *promise* of prayer.

Verse 6 continues, *"...and thy Father which seeth in secret shall reward thee openly."*

1. When our prayer meets the conditions we have

already discussed, it is our Father's pleasure to answer.

2. When we pray and don't receive an answer, we need to review our prayer and our lives to find where we may not have met the Biblical conditions.

3. If we dont' find the cause for delay, we must simply continue to pray faithfully and learn to "wait on the Lord."

G. The *plan* of prayer.

Matthew 5:7 gives a clear plan for our prayers.

1. They should be plain, simple and to the point.

2. We don't get God's attention by long repetitions or the use of vain words. God looks beyond those things and into our heart.

3. We need to make sure that our heart and our faith is behind our praying. Our heart and life need to be "prayer-conditioned!"

SUMMARY: When it comes to prayer, there is always *our part* and *God's part.* Our part is to do what we can do, then trust God to do what is beyond our ability. It isn't fair to God for us to sit back and ask Him to do what is within our ability to do.

There is a story of a bar that was built right next door to a little community church. The church began to meet together to pray that the Lord would close down the bar. They prayed for quite some time, until late one night they heard the sound of the town fire engine making its way toward the church. There, next to the little church building, the bar was engulfed in flames. The church members soon gathered together and watched the scene. Someone remarked how God had finally come through and answered their prayers. Standing in the crowd was an elderly saint who said, "Well, I don't mean to take anything away from God, but while you folks were praying I was putting 'legs' on my prayers!"

Of course, no Christian should advocate burning down bars, but the principle illustrated in this story is important. There are things we ought to do, and there are things God must do for us in answer to our prayers. We need to learn to pray as though everything depends upon God, and work as though everything depends upon us. That's an unbeatable philosophy for the Christian life.

REFLECTIONS: Answer the following questions individually or in class. Give careful attention to your answers. This exercise is what the Bible refers to as *meditation.* Think on these things....

1. What does the Bible mean when it says that Daniel had a "custom" of prayer? What was his custom?

_____

_____

2. When the King passed a law against prayer, what did Daniel do? Was it right for him to do this since the law of the land

was declared? Why?

_____

_____

3. List at least three hinderances to prayers.

_____

_____

4. In your mind, what are the key elements of good prayer?

_____

_____

5. What is the first and most important prayer one ought to pray?

_____

_____

6. In Psalm 51 we read King David's prayer of repentance. What was it David had lost and was seeking through his prayer?

_____

_____

7. List several things that can be accomplished through effective prayer.

_____

_____

8. In Matthew 5:7 our Lord gives us a key element in prayer. What is He teaching us in this important verse?

_____

_____

9. What is the "secret" of prayer?

_____

_____

10. We must learn to _____like everything depends upon God and _____like everything depends upon us.

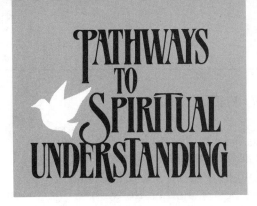

LESSON 9

Giving and Stewardship

MAIN SCRIPTURES:
MALACHI 3:7-12; LUKE 16:1-13;
I CORINTHIANS 16:1-2

LESSON AIM: To reach a Biblical understanding of what it means to be a *steward,* who is called a steward, and what the obligations of a steward are to the master. To relate this knowledge to the present-day responsibility of giving in support of God's work. To understand God's promises to those who are concerned about being good stewards.

SUGGESTED MEMORY VERSES:
II Corinthians 9:6; Proverbs 3:9-10; Luke 6:38; Proverb 11:25; Luke 16:10

OVERVIEW:
   I. THE DEFINITION AND MEANING OF A STEWARD
  II. BIBLICAL PRINCIPLES OF STEWARDSHIP
 III. THE BASICS OF GIVING TO THE LORD

INTRODUCTION: In the Bible, 38 parables of Jesus are recorded. Out of those, 12 deal with the subject of stewardship. That's about one-third of the total parables recorded in Scripture! Evidently, stewardship is an important topic for the Christian to study. Your entire life, here on this earth and later in eternity, will be affected by your understanding or misunderstanding of this topic.

The Bible teaches that man came into this world empty (without material goods), and that when he departs for eternity, he can carry no goods beyond the grave. However, there is a method, according to the Bible, of "laying up in store" for eternity.

Learn how to prepare now for that time now—by studying the principles of stewardship found in the Bible, and applying them to daily life. The life of a good steward is rich and full. The good steward is one who has committed his life, lands, and goods into the Lord's hands and trusts God for complete supply of all his needs. Very few believers ever really learn how to become good stewards. Yet, the best of God's blessings are reserved for those who will.

(Where lines are provided after a Scripture reference, look up the verse and write a one sentence summary of what the Scripture is saying to you.)

I. THE DEFINITION AND MEANING OF A STEWARD

A. The word *"steward,"* as used in the Bible, comes from two Greek words that, together, mean *"house-manager."*

1. According to the Bible, a steward was one who administered the goods of another. He was the manager of the household.

2. In simple terms, it means that God made you the manager of the goods and abilities He has placed into your hands.

   a. Remember, you came into this world with nothing, and when you leave, you must leave it all behind.

   b. Everything placed in your hands between birth and death is simply loaned to you by God to enrich your life here upon the earth.

   c. You are to use a portion of your goods and talents to serve and work for Him.

   d. You are a household manager of all that God gives to you.

3. List some of the things God has placed into your hands, thus making you His steward. (Don't forget, children are loaned by God.)

   _____

   _____

4. Understanding the principle behind the meaning of *"steward"* is necessary for a proper understanding of every other Biblical principle related to stewardship.

   a. Make sure you understand what a steward is before you go on to the principles of stewardship.

   b. Remember, a steward is one who manages the goods and properties of another. It's the responsibility of a good steward to use those goods for the best return to his master.

II. BIBLICAL PRINCIPLES OF STEWARDSHIP

A. God is the sole owner of all things!

1. If you don't come to terms with this principle you'll never be a good steward.

   a. Misunderstanding this first principle leads to the sins of covetousness and discontentment. It's imperative, therefore that you do not mistake this precept.

   b. God is the original owner of everything. Man does not really own anything.

2. This principle is taught in Scripture after Scripture.

   a. Leviticus 25:23 _____

   _____

(Note, the land is the Lord's.)

b. Haggai 2:8 *"The silver is mine, the gold is mine, saith the Lord of hosts."* (Even the mineral deposits belong to the Lord!)

c. Psalm 24:1 _____

_____

d. Not only is the land the Lord's but the *"fullness thereof"* is also His. That means that everything in and on the land is the Lord's.

e. We can take it one step further. In Romans 14:8, we find that *we* belong to the Lord.

3. The reason Job was able to overcome all the trials and losses he suffered was because he recognized that God was the owner of all the possessions he had held, and it was God's sovereign right to do with those possessions as He chose.

a. Job 1:21 _____

_____

_____

b. Notice, Job's attitude in his time of loss was that the Lord had given, and the Lord had taken away. (The Lord only took what He had given, therefore it was the Lord's, not Job's.)

c. Job 1:22 shows an attitude that Christians should try to imitate when they suffer times of loss.

B. God expects His stewards to use His goods and abilities in a way that He would approve.

In Bible times, a good steward was one who managed and used the goods of his master to bring glory, blessing, honor and gain to his master. Not only was this the duty of a good steward, but this is also the duty of a good Christian!

You'll never be blessed of God and have a life of contentment and joy until you grasp the first principle of stewardship and submit your life, lands, family and goods to God's ownership.

1. Read the parable found in Luke 16:1-13. The steward got into trouble with his master only after he misused his master's goods.

a. In Luke 16:1, the master accused the steward of wasting his goods.

b. According to verse 2, he was in danger of being removed from his place of stewardship because of his careless attitude.

2. To use the goods and abilities that God gives you only for your own sake and advantage would be completely dishonest.

a. We must be sure we understand that it is God who gives us the ability to work and to earn.

b. Read Deuteronomy 8:18. The Bible tells us not to forget who it is that gives us our ability.

3. God gives us our talents for three primary uses.
    a. To earn a living so that we can supply our daily needs (like food, clothing and shelter).
    b. To be able to afford "extras." (Read I Timothy 6:17.) Enjoying life isn't wrong, as long as we don't fall into the trap of loving our pleasures more than we love God!
    c. To return a portion to Him to carry out His work at home and around the world. (Read I Chronicles 29:14, paying special attention to the last portion of the verse.)

4. Certainly, in the work of God, stewardship involves more than just money.
    a. Stewardship involves things like time, talents and abilities.
    b. If you give of your money and excuse yourself from serving God with your time and abilities, you aren't an honest steward.
    c. Don't rob God of the skills, talents and gifts He has given you. These things, too, must be used to bring honor and glory to Him in order to be called a good steward.

C. How we manage and use the things God places in our hands today determines what He will give us tomorrow.

1. Luke 16:10-11 sets forth this principle perfectly.
    a. Verse 11 _____

    _____

    b. God returns His blessings to us in relation to our faithfulness toward those things He has already placed into our hands.
    c. We must learn to be faithful even in the small things committed to us. (Things like a Sunday school class, or a place in the choir.)
    d. If God is to extend "great" things to us, we must first be faithful in the small things.

2. The law of *sowing and reaping* is a Bible principle connected with stewardship.
    a. Read II Corinthians 9:6-8. Write verse 6. _____

    _____

    _____

    b. The *harvest* is always determined by the *sowing*.
    c. We cannot expect to reap more than we sow. We certainly cannot expect to reap in an area where we haven't sown at all!
    d. God is never going to give us more than He can trust us with. If we are unfaithful in the administration of what we have today, He won't bestow extra to us tomorrow.
    e. The fastest way to increase your blessings from God is to learn to be content with what you

now have, and to use it wisely to bring glory and honor to Him.

f.   Every parent has used this same principle in training children. We don't give a 10-year-old child $50 at a time to spend at the store. Children that age aren't mature enough to spend it carefully and wisely. We start children out with, perhaps, 25¢ at a time until they grow and mature. As they become mature and trustworthy, we give them more and more.

g.   The amount of talent, goods or funds that our heavenly Father gives each of us in the future is determined by our faithfulness in that which He has given us today.

h.   We must learn to be content, generous and faithful if we want to grow more mature in stewardship.

D.   All of us will, someday, be called to stand before the Lord and give account of our stewardship. II Corinthians 5:10

_____

_____

1.   Both believers and non-believers will stand before the judgment seat of Christ.

a.   For believers, this isn't a judgment to determine eternal destiny, rather to give account of their lives' works.

b.   We must give account of all that God has placed into our hands.

c.   We will only answer for ourselves and the abilities, skills, talents, goods and possessions that God gave us.

1.   Someone else may have been given 10 talents by the Lord while we may have received only five.

2.   We'll only be required to answer for the five talents that we were given, not the 10 given to another.

d.   Therefore, this time of judgment will be completely fair for all of God's people. (Read Romans 14:12.)

e.   Only the dishonest and unfaithful steward needs to worry about standing before the master and giving account of his stewardship. If we endeavor to love and serve the Lord to the best of the abilities and talents He has given us, we need not worry or fear the day we will stand before Him.

III. THE BASICS OF GIVING TO THE LORD

Read Malachi 3:7-12. A number of people today, having been disappointed by some pastor or evangelist, stop giving to the work of God. And in many cases churches and ministries faced with declining offerings resort to unscriptural methods to raise funds. Both of these attitudes and practices are wrong. God's Word is very clear about giving. We need not be ashamed to preach or to practice what God has ordained.

Malachi was the last of the Old Testament-era prophets. People in his day were very much like people today. Their attitudes caused dark clouds of unbelief to settle upon the land. The religious leaders failed to preach the Word of God, and as a result, God's people fell into idolatry and backsliding. Their backsliding was made evident by the fact that they forsook God's house and kept the portion of goods that belonged to God. God sent Malachi to the people. He preached concerning revival and how to get the blessing of God back in their lives. Part of Malachi's message centered on giving.

Every Christian must understand the basics of giving (as outlined in the Book of Malachi) in order to become a good steward.

A. Giving to God

1. The basis, or foundation, for all giving to the Lord is found in Malachi 3:10, specifically, in the word *"tithes."*
   a. The word *tithe* means "tenth part."
   b. The tithe is the basis of *all* of our other giving.

2. Tithing isn't an issue of the Hebrew law. It began almost 400 years before the law was established.
   a. Abraham gave a tithe (as God's portion) to honor God. Later, God established this same giving principle as part of the law.
   b. Jesus added his approval to the giving of the tithe in His day. (Matthew 23:23. Note the words, *"These ought ye to have done."*)

3. If we believe that the entire Bible is to be read and held as the Word of God, we must believe the Old Testament as well as the New Testament.
   a. Read Leviticus 27:30-31 and you will clearly see that the tithe is the Lord's.
   b. In fact, we really do not *give* the tithe; we simply remove our hands from that which is already God's portion.

4. The result of keeping the tithe is found in Malachi 3:9.
   a. According to the Bible it results in the curse of God.
   b. It is called the sin of robbing God.

5. The reason for bringing the tithe to the storehouse is found in Malachi, chapter 3.
   a. Verse 10 says, *"that there may be meat (provision) in mine house...."*
   b. The tithe is God's approved method of supply for His work to be done.
   c. If every believer would at least tithe, most churches would never have a financial need.

6. This passage of Scripture also tells where to give the tithe.
    a. Verse 10 teaches that the tithe is to be brought into God's storehouse.
    b. There is little disagreement that the storehouse was in the temple.
    c. Simply put, the tithe was to be brought to the "Church" and given to the work of God.
    d. Read I Corinthians 16:1-2.

B. Barriers to giving. (What hinders some people from giving scripturally to God?)

1. Sometimes it's a lack of Biblical understanding.
    a. This is the reason pastors and teachers must not fear teaching what the Bible has to say about giving.
    b. It would be a shame for some to miss out on the blessings of giving because they have never been taught the Bible.

2. Backsliding is a barrier to giving.
    When a Christian neglects the house of God, daily devotions and prayer, giving to God usually also ceases.

3. Misplaced affection becomes a barrier to the blessing of giving.
    a. This principle is taught in I Timothy 6:9-10.
    b. Many have replaced their love for the Lord with a love for money and the things that money can buy for them.

4. Selfishness is a barrier that will block the blessings that come from giving.
    a. The Bible tells us, *"It is more blessed to give than to receive."* Yet many never really learn the blessedness of giving because they are too selfish.
    b. Giving becomes easy when you put your heart into things of God! (Just like a mother who gives of herself to her family day after day because she has a love and devoted attachment that motivates her.)
    c. Do you rejoice when you put an offering into the plate on Sunday? Or does your mind wander to those things the money could have purchased for your own enjoyment? Be careful that a selfish heart doesn't become a barrier to your giving.

C. The blessings to be found in giving to God.

1. The blessings of giving far outweigh the losses when it comes to giving to the Lord.
    God will be no man's debtor. As you learn to honor and obey the Lord concerning giving you'll find abundant blessings.

2. There are several blessings promised by God and found in Malachi, chapter 3. Malachi 3 holds a direct challenge from God to all of us. In this challenge, God offers three promises of blessing.
    a. First, verse 10 *"I will open the windows of heaven...."* is a reference to God sending a time of revival, and refreshing His people.
    b. The second is found in verse 11. *"I will rebuke the devourer for your sakes...."* This is a reference to God's ability to keep the "wolf away from the door." His ability extends to being able to bless even in a time of recession.
    c. The last blessing is also found in verse 11. It refers to God blessing the ground of the one who will trust and give. This is a simple reference to God's blessings upon our endeavors, to make them fruitful.

3. There are many, many more promises of blessing found throughout the Bible which are related to the matter of faithful giving.
    a. Read Proverbs 3:9-10, Proverb 11:25 and Luke 6:38.
    b. Giving in order to receive isn't a proper motive. But, giving, in order to receive, in order to give again, is!
    c. Why not trust God and take Him at His word? Take the challenge found in Malachi 3:10 and 11, and put His wonderful promises to the test.

SUMMARY: I Timothy 6:7 says, *"For we brought nothing into this world, and it is certain we can carry nothing out."* That is an absolute truth! Everything we have in our hands between the time we arrive in this world and the time we leave this world was put there by God. He's the sole owner of everything. We who are believers are His stewards or, the managers of goods that belong to Him. Our goal ought to be excellence in our stewardship.

Though we can carry nothing out of this world, we're told in the Bible that we can "send things on ahead." Matthew 6:20 says, *"But lay up for yourselves treasures in heaven, where neither moth nor rust doth corrupt, and where thieves do not break though and steal."* By investing in the work of God both with your abilities and with your funds, you are "laying up treaures in heaven."

The story is told of a wealthy, but miserly Christian man who was accustomed to all the finer things of this life. However, he was known to be selfish, especially with giving to the work of God. Then came the day that he died. The miser found himself in heaven, where an angel met him by the gate. The angel informed him that he had been sent to escort him to his new home.

As they walked down the beautiful avenues of Heaven, the miser gazed upon row after row of mansions far more beautiful than the home he had lived in on the earth. He was filled with anxious anticipation as he thought of where his mansion was and what it must look like. He figured with the lifestyle he had grown used to on the earth, the Lord must have made a very special mansion for his eternal home.

Finally, they crossed to the last street in heaven and went to the far back lot. There sat a very humble little one-room house—not much better than the tool shed on the miser's earthly property. The man was shocked and demanded to know why his home in heaven looked so poor compared to all the rest. To this, the angel replied, "Oh, you see, we did the very best job we could with the materials you sent ahead."

Our home in heaven isn't dependent upon our works, but upon God's saving grace given to us in Christ Jesus. But, what if it *were* that way in heaven? What if our home in heaven was being built by the materials we sent ahead? What kind of eternal home would we have by the time we arrived? Let us learn to "set our affections on things above, not on things on the earth," and ask God to help us live the life of a good and faithful steward so that we may stand before Him unashamed someday.

REFLECTIONS: Answer the following questions individually or in class. Give careful attention to your answers. This exercise is what the Bible refers to as *meditation*. Think on these things....

1. Almost one-third of all the parables of Jesus deal with stewardship. Why do you think the Lord has placed such as emphasis on this topic?

   _____

   _____

2. What does the Greek word translated *steward* mean in the English language? What does this mean to you?

   _____

   _____

3. What does a steward own?

   _____

   _____

4. At what point in Job's life did he display a wonderful example of being a good and faithful steward?

   _____

   _____

5. For what reasons has God given us the ability to earn "gain" (or to make money)?

   _____

   _____

6. What does stewardship involve, other than money?

   _____

   _____

7. Is there ever a day of judgment for stewards? If so, what is it
   called? What is the factor that determines our judgment?

   _____

   _____

8. What does the word *tithe* mean? When was tithing first
   practiced in the Bible?

   _____

   _____

9. What are some of the barriers to giving to the work of God?

   _____

   _____

10. Why is stewardship so connected with our love for God?

    _____

    _____

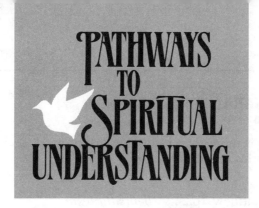

LESSON 10

Your Service to the Lord

MAIN SCRIPTURES:
ROMANS 12:1-21; ACTS 8:1-8
II TIMOTHY 2:1-7

LESSON AIM: To lead to the understanding of what it means to be a true disciple of Jesus. To understand what things are necessary to equip one to be effective in this service.

SUGGESTED MEMORY VERSES:
Ephesians 2:10; Matthew 9:37; II Timothy 2:15; Philippians 4:13; John 15:8.

OVERVIEW:

    I. THE QUALIFYING CHARACTERISTICS OF A DISCIPLE

   II. A GOOD DISCIPLE WILL ALSO BE A GOOD SOLDIER

  III. THE CHRISTIAN'S SERVICE TO THE KING

  IV. HOW TO BE EFFECTIVE IN SERVICE TO THE LORD

INTRODUCTION: The ninth chapter of the Gospel of John tells a wonderful story of a man whom Jesus healed of blindness. What a great day it was for him when he met Jesus, the Son of God! As he went on his way, leaping for joy and praising the Lord, he ran into the Pharisees who criticized him for such behavior on the Sabbath day. They asked him who had made his blind eyes see and who he believed Jesus to be. His classic answer is found in verse 25. We find his own cutting question directed to the Pharisees in the last portion of verse 27: *"Will ye also be His disciples?"*

That is the main question of this lesson— will you truly be a disciple of Jesus? If so, you must understand what it really means to be a disciple. What is the duty of a disciple? What is the service we ought to render to the Lord? If we are going to serve Him, how can we be effective in our service?

There are far too many people today who want to sit at the table of God's blessings but are not willing to go out into the field and help do the work of God.

Often-times, people start out to serve the Lord, but soon give up and resign themselves to becoming a spectator in the arena of Christian service. Why is that so? That, along with other questions will be considered in this lesson.

(Where lines are provided after a Scripture reference, look up the verse and write a one sentence summary of what this Scripture is saying to you.)

I. THE QUALIFYING CHARACTERISTICS OF A DISCIPLE

Being a disciple of Jesus is more than just being saved. There are many characteristics found in the Bible.

A. A disciple denies self.

1. Read and fill in Matthew 16:24. *"Then said Jesus unto his disciples, 'If any man will come after me*

_____

_____

_____ . '"

a. A true disciple is one who is acquainted with self-denial.

b. Self-denial goes against human nature and therefore, is something we must learn if we are going to be a disciple.

2. To deny self means to put the Lord's will over and above your own will.

It means to love the Lord more than any material possession, and to have a desire to live a life pleasing to Him.

3. You do not lose or miss out on life when you decide to live the life of a disciple.

a. Luke 9:24 _____

_____

_____

b. The secret to living the life of a joyous Christian is found in the above verse.

c. To "lose one's life" for Jesus' sake is to live life each day for His sake, to bring honor and glory to Him in all that one does or says.

d. You cannot be a disciple without self-denial.

B. A disciple bears his cross.

1. According to Jesus, in Matthew 16:24, after self-denial comes cross-bearing.

a. Some think that this means the Christian life is a burden.

b. That isn't the teaching of the Bible. The Word of God teaches that the life of a Christian is one characterized by joy and blessing, not burden and hardship.

c. Cross-bearing means finding God's will for your life and doing it completely and faithfully.

d. That's exactly what Jesus did. John 6:38 _____

_____

_____

e. The cross was God's will for His Son Jesus. If there was a cross for Jesus, there is also a cross which represents the Father's will for our lives.

f.   In other words, there is a mission for your life if you are saved. You cannot truly be a disciple unless you are concerned about doing the will of God.

C.   A disciple is one who endeavors to follow Jesus as an example in lifestyle.

    1.   Notice the last part of Matthew 16:24 says, *"...and follow me."*

        a.   A true disciple learns all he can about Jesus, and then endeavors to live as He lived.

        b.   In days past this was called *"separation."* It was understood that a Christian lived a life of separation from this world.

        c.   This doesn't mean that we're to be "above" the world, but that we're to be different from the world.

        d.   As Christians, we mustn't allow the world to dictate our music, dress, styles, amusements, or even our vocabulary.

        e.   Read John 17:14. Write the teaching of this verse. _____

_____

_____

        f.   A disciple will be more concerned about pleasing the Lord than seeking the approval of the world.

        g.   In Romans 12:2 we're instructed *"...be not conformed to this world...."* What does that mean to you? _____

_____

_____

        h.   We, as Christians, aren't to be overly pious or overzealous in the eyes of the world; but neither should we be overly concerned about the approval of the world.

        i.   A disciple endeavors to follow Jesus as an example in speech, attitudes and deeds.

D.   A disciple loves the brethren.

    1.   Read John 13:34-35 and write it's teaching. _____

_____

_____

        a.   A disciple has a genuine love for the people of God, regardless of their age, race, color or denomination. We're to love the brethren (those who have been saved by the Grace of God).

        b.   This love needs to manifest itself in a sweet spirit and in deeds of kindness to others.

        c.   Love cannot be seen, therefore it must be shown. We show our love by our actions.

    E.   A disciple bears fruit in his life.

        1.   John 15:8 _____

             _____

             _____

             a.   Our Father in heaven is glorified when our lives "bear fruit".

             b.   Bearing fruit is an evidence of discipleship, and the duty of every Christian.

        2.   There are two types of fruit God wants to see from our lives.

             a.   There is the inward fruit of good character and godly conduct.

                 1.   This list is found in Galatians 5:22-23

                 2.   It includes love, joy, peace, longsuffering, gentleness, goodness, faith, meekness and temperance.

                 3.   The Holy Spirit wants to develop our character in these areas if we will practice these attributes and pray about them.

             b.   Bearing fruit also includes bringing others to Christ.

                 1.   A true disciple is concerned about the souls of others and will witness for Christ's sake whenever the Holy Spirit opens the door of opportunity.

                 2.   Read John 1:40-42 and you will see how natural it is for a disciple to have the desire to bring others to the Savior.

    F.   A true disciple knows the One whom he follows.

        There are many today who claim to be disciples of Jesus but in reality don't even know Him as Savior.

        1.   Do you know Christ (not just historically, but personally)?

             If you have any doubt at all about His question, go back and review the lesson on the "New Birth." It will teach you from the truth of God's Word how you can know that you are a child of God.

        2.   The first step to becoming a real disciple of Jesus is to know the One you want to follow as your very own Savior.

II. A GOOD DISCIPLE WILL ALSO BE A GOOD SOLDIER

    Read II Timothy 2:1-7. The Bible compares the life of a Christian to the life of a soldier. A soldier is one who serves his country. Since this lesson concerns the subject of service, we need to know some things about being a good soldier of the Lord.

    A.   The soldier's ***task.***

        A soldier has two basic duties in life.

1. The first duty is to follow orders.
    a. A good soldier will follow every order to the very best of his ability.
    b. As good soldiers of the Lord, we must do our best to follow the orders of the Lord.
    c. We have an entire manual given to us by our Commander-in-Chief. It's called the Bible! We need to study it carefully so we can follow its orders.
2. The other basic duty of a soldier is to fight.
    a. As Christians we're involved in "spiritual battle."
    b. According to I Timothy 6:12 we are to *"fight the good fight of faith,"* That means we are to be willing to contend for our faith and fight to save it for future generations.
    c. When the Apostle Paul came to the last days he had upon the earth, he said that he had fought a good fight. (II Timothy 4:7)

B. The soldier's *training.*

    Every good soldier must spend time in a training program that will help prepare him to serve.
    We, as good soldiers, must also take time to train by studying our Bible.

1. A good training program instructs in discipline.
    a. Discipline is the very first attribute taught a soldier.
    b. There is a time to go to bed, a time to rise in the morning, a time to eat, a time to work and a time for rest.
    c. I Corinthians 9:25 teaches us that a Christian should lead a disciplined life. _____
        _____
        _____
2. A good training program instructs in dedication.
    a. A good soldier must be dedicated to his duty. You will not have to look for him at his appointed time, nor will you have to force him to do what he ought to do.
    b. Dedication to duty will also be the mark of a good soldier in the Lord's army!
3. The training program of a soldier teaches him denial.
    a. A good soldier learns to leave all behind when he is on the field of service.
    b. He serves in the heat of the sun and in the cold of winter's snow. He doesn't serve just in the days of ease, but in difficult times too. He must learn to leave behind all personal desires when duty calls.

C. The soldier's tools.

1. No soldier is sent into battle without the tools that

equip him to do his job properly.

Likewise, God has supplied the tools that every Christian "soldier" needs to get the job done.

2. The Christian's tools are spiritual tools.
    a. II Corinthians 10:3-4 _____

    _____

    _____

    b. They are mighty and powerful!

3. The Christian's tools are special tools.
    a. Read Ephesians 6:16-17. We have been given a very special suit of armor for our stand against the spiritual enemy.
    b. We have been given only one weapon in this spiritual battle—the Word of God. It's the only weapon that we'll need if we're skilled in its use.
    c. A good soldier keeps his weapon close at hand and knows how to use it when the enemy attacks.

4. We have also been given *special agents* to help us in our battles.
    a. Psalm 34:7 _____

    _____

    _____

    b. God has assigned special angel agents to guard and protect His own.
    c. Read II Kings 6:8-23. You'll find a wonderful story of how God dispatched many special agents to help protect one of His faithful soldiers.

5. The Christian's tools are successful tools.
    a. Read Ephesians 6:10-11. The Bible says, *"...that ye may be able to stand against the wiles of the devil."*
    b. The Bible teaches us that if we learn to use the armor and weapon that God has provided, we **will be able to stand!**

D. The soldier's testings.

1. The life of a soldier won't always be the life of ease. Every now and then the soldier faces a trial or a battle.

2. Likewise, the life of a Christian will sometimes lead through a time of battle.

    If we're prepared and understand that this is common to all Christians, the devil won't be able to defeat and discourage us in our time of trial.

3. Some battles will be physical.
    a. Since we live in a mortal body, we'll suffer through some times of sickness and weakness in our body.

    b.   This is common to all of us since we live in a body that is aging and is on its march to the grave.

    c.   We needn't let this discourage us. The Apostle Paul fought the same battle. (Read II Corinthians 12:7-10.)

    d.   We need to learn to pray through times of physical illness and to keep our spirit strong so the devil won't cause us to become bitter and defeated.

4.   Some battles will be mental.

    a.   The devil wants to get into your mind and defeat your spirit with thoughts that are either wicked or discouraging.

    b.   Learn to stand at the door of your mind and guard your thoughts!

    c.   Read Philippians 4:8 and follow it daily.

5.   Some battles will be spiritual.

    a.   The devil will attack your home, your testimony and even your church.

    b.   There is strength in unity with others. Use that knowledge to guard against the spiritual attacks of the enemy.

E.   The soldier's triumph.

1.   When the battle is over and the soldier comes home, He deserves a welcome and a time of rest.

    a.   Our soldier's received a great welcome when they came home after World War II.

    b.   Every soldier who braves battle and gives his best to stand against the enemy deserves the same kind of welcome.

2.   Three words characterize the life of the Apostle Paul, who was noted to be a good soldier of the Lord while he lived.

    a.   The first word is *fight*. He said, *"I have fought a good fight."* He gave his best!

    b.   The second word is *finished*. He declared that he had finished his course. He didn't drop out or give up in the time of trial.

    c.   The last word is *faithful*. He said that he had *"kept the faith."* He remained faithful, even when others gave up.

3.   Here is some wonderful news—*"Henceforth there is laid up for me a crown of righteousness"* (II Timothy 4:8).

    a.   Paul knew he was going to receive the reward of a good soldier.

    b.   He wasn't thinking about his trials, his hardships, or his battles; he was thinking about Heaven!

    c.   A good soldier keeps his mind on Heaven and doesn't give up in the battle! That is the cure for spiritual "battle fatigue."

III. THE CHRISTIAN'S SERVICE TO THE KING

Read Romans 12:1-21. This chapter has the most complete teaching on the Christian life contained in one chapter of the Bible. This chapter teaches us about consecration, working with others, and even our attitude toward and treatment of those who mistreat us. There is a lot that could be studied in this chapter, but we will concentrate on the little phrase in verse 11 that says, *"...serving the Lord."*

God has given us the privilege of serving Him. There are five things we need to consider in our service.

A.   The call to serve.

    1.   Romans 12:1-2 tells the Christian that he is to present his body to the Lord as a living sacrifice.
      That means we are to give ourselves to the Lord's service and be willing to do whatever we can for His sake.

    2.   When Jesus began His earthly ministry, He walked by the shores of Galilee. There He called men like Peter, Andrew, James and John to follow Him. Why?
      a.   He needed to use them in His work.
      b.   His need for people to serve Him hasn't changed today. God still needs Christians to serve Him. We have already been called!
      c.   Matthew 9:37 _____

      _____

      _____

      d.   Ephesians 2:10 teaches that we have been saved in order to serve the Lord (*"Created unto good works."*).

    3.   Often people say, "What a privilege it would have been to be a James or John or Peter." But you and I have the same privilege to serve the same Lord as did these men.

B.   The place to serve.

    1.   Not only has the Lord given us the privilege of service, but He designated a central place of service. That place is the Church.
      If Christ loved the Church so much that he died for its formation, you and I need to love the Church enough to offer our service to the Lord through it.

    2.   Many Christians have an entirely wrong concept of the purpose of the Church.
      a.   The Church doesn't exist to serve us, or to care only for our needs. It isn't a place to go find spiritual entertainment. The Church exists to bring glory and honor to the Lord!
      Ephesians 3:21 _____

      _____

      _____

    b.   We bring glory to the Lord by serving Him through the ministries of the local church.

    c.   To spiritualize what a past president said, "We ought not ask what our church can do for us, but what we can do for our church."

C.   Instructions for service.

    God would not call us to serve Him, and give us a place to serve Him, without also giving us the instructions on how to carry out His work.
    II Timothy 2:15 _____

_____

_____

    1.   What would cause a workman to be ashamed? Wouldn't it be that he didn't know how to do what he was employed to do?

    2.   Likewise, the Bible has been given to us to teach us how to carry out the work of God. We must study it faithfully lest we be ashamed in not knowing how to do what God has commissioned us to do.

    3.   The Bible is a complete instruction manual. It teaches us how to go to heaven, how to live a joyful life, how to have a blessed home and marriage, how to build our church, how to bring others to Christ, how to overcome things like worry, fear and temptation, and how to do the work of God!

D.   The power for service.

    1.   Our Lord wouldn't give us a great work to do without also giving us the power to get it done.

        a.   You need not labor in your power only. God has provided His power through the help of the Holy Spirit.

        b.   Matthew 28:18 _____

_____

_____

            Notice from this passage that we are to go in the power of God.

        c.   Philippians 4:13 _____

_____

_____

            It is Christ who will "strengthen" or empower us to do all things in His name.

        d.   Many Christians grow frustrated and weary in their service to the Lord. Often it's because they're trying to serve the Lord, but not in the power of the Holy Spirit. We need His power to do His work!

E.   The purpose for service.

1. God has a purpose and a reason for everything He does.
    a. Everybody needs to have a purpose and a cause that motivates them to operate.
    b. God has saved us and given us a purpose in our service to Him.

2. Those who have been saved by God's grace have three primary purposes in life.
    a. To bring glory to God through their lives.
        1. This is our first and greatest purpose in life!
        2. I Corinthians 10:31 _____

        _____

        _____

    b. To exhort, edify and encourage one another through life.
        1. Galatians 6:2 _____

        _____

        _____

        2. One thing that will keep life filled with joy is to search out someone every day to whom you can be a help and a blessing.
    c. To carry the Gospel to those without Christ, that they, too, may be saved.
        1. Acts 8:4 _____

        _____

        _____

        2. The greatest thing a Christian can do is to bring others to Christ. We need to do that through our collective service in church ministries and missions, and also through personal evangelism. There is no greater service to the King than this!

IV. HOW TO BE EFFECTIVE IN SERVICE TO THE LORD

Read Acts 8:1-8. In this chapter of the Bible we meet a man named Phillip. Phillip was a man who had learned to be effective in the Lord's work. He didn't possess anything that you and I don't have. What he did, you and I can do—if we'll learn some basics about service.

If we're going to serve the Lord, we ought to be effective in our service. Otherwise we've simply wasted effort.

A lot of the service in church ministry is rendered out of duty or routine and, therefore, loses its effectiveness. We need to be "wholehearted" in what we do for our Lord.

The Lord's work includes everything from parking cars, ushering, keeping a nursery, cleaning the buildings, teaching a class, greeting visitors, driving a bus, and singing in the choir, to anything else that goes into the operation of the church and its ministries. God has no second class duties. Everything we do is vital and important and how we do what we do determines our effectiveness. There are six things necessary if we want our work to be more effective.

A.   We must work *envisioned.*

   1.   Why is it so important to have a vision?
      a.   Because you will never do more than your vision.
      b.   Proverb 29:18 _____

         _____

         _____

   2.   Having a vision is vital to the Lord's work and to your effectiveness.
      a.   Success in ministry isn't wicked, nor is it instant.
      b.   It isn't wrong to have a desire to be successful in our ministries, as long as our desire is to give God all the glory.
      c.   We need to be able to "see" our classrooms filled and "see" our church filled Sunday after Sunday. "See" things in your heart or you will never see them in reality.
      d.   Don't ever let the devil steal your vision of doing great things for God. A vision is necessary to achieve your goals.

B.   We must work with *enthusiasm.*

   1.   When Phillip "hit the streets" of Samaria, he was excited about what he was doing.
      Those who serve the Lord without zeal and enthusiasm imply to others that the work of God isn't very important.

   2.   The word *enthusiasm* means: to have an excited zeal for a purpose or a cause.
      a.   Anyone attending a sporting event, or watching one on television sees the stands filled with thousands of people who are enthused about what is taking place.
      b.   Go to church on Sunday and you'll sometimes find those who seem to be very unexcited about what is taking place.
      c.   If ever there was a place and a purpose for enthusiasm, it's in the work of God.
      d.   We need to "show" others that we are excited about what God is able to do in the lives of those who meet Him.
      e.   Notice from Acts 8:8 the attitude in Samaria after Phillip arrived. The city was filled with joy.
      f.   May God help us to serve Him with enthusiasm!

C.   We must work with *energy.*

1. We need to learn to put our heart into whatever we do for the Lord's sake.

    a. Too often, we do only what will get us by, and even that isn't filled with energy.
    b. We must learn to tap into God's source of strength and serve Him with our energy.

D. We must work with *endurance.*

    If we are to be effective, we must *"run with patience the race that is set before us."*

    1. Read Hebrews 12:1 _____

        _____

        _____

        a. We need to learn how to endure!
        b. Remember, there is always a season of time between the planting and the harvest.
        c. It is often during this time that God's people get weary and give up in their service. How many quit right on the verge of the harvest?

    2. We must remain steadfast in our labors. Read I Corinthians 15:58. _____

        _____

        _____

        a. No one ever reaches a goal without the character to endure. So it is with service to the Lord.
        b. God doesn't reward results, He rewards faithfulness!

E. We need to learn to work with *enjoyment.*

    1. Even the difficult tasks in life can be made enjoyable to the one who learns to conquer his or her attitudes.

        a. Take, for example, women who serve their families day in and day out by doing the same chores over and over again.
        b. What is it that motivates a wife and mother to serve like that? It's her love for her husband and her family.
        c. What is it that will make the duties of a Christian seem like a delight? It's a deep love for the Lord.
        d. Psalm 100:2 _____

            _____

            _____

    2. We will be much more effective in our service to the Lord when we learn to mirror the gladness in our heart and allow it to characterize our service.

        If we show the world a smile even on difficult days, we will attract more people to the Savior.

F.   We must work with *earnestness.*

1.   This means that we must understand the urgency of the Lord's work and attend to our work with seriousness.

a.   John 9:4 _____

_____

_____

b.   The night is coming when our work time will be past. Therefore, we must give our earnest attention to what we are doing for Christ's sake.

2.   James 4:14 teaches us that our life is like a *"vapour that appeareth for a little time, and then vanisheth away."*

Life is brief at best, and we must not waste any opportunity given to us to serve the Lord.

SUMMARY: In 1977 a bus-ministry worker knocked on the door of a home and invited the children living there to ride his bus and attend Sunday school. The following Sunday, three children in this family went to church aboard his bus. The oldest girl, who was only 12 years old at that time, came to know Jesus as her Savior during her first month of attending church. She rode the bus faithfully thereafter until the winter of 1980, when, one week before Christmas, she died in her sleep. Thank God for the bus workers and the Sunday school teachers who worked hand-in-hand to bring her to the Savior.

There is no work more important than the work of the Lord. It is the only work that will continue to reap dividends into eternity. We need to renew our commitment to serve the Lord, and we need to do it faithfully and effectively. Don't let the devil discourage you from service to the Lord. It's a wonderful work. You can be assured that your labor "in" the Lord is not in vain!

REFLECTIONS: Answer the following questions individually or in class. Give careful attention to your answers. This exercise is what the Bible refers to as *meditation.* Think on these things....

1.   According to Jesus, what is the very first qualification of a disciple? What does this mean to you?

_____

_____

2.   What does the Bible mean concerning the cross that we must bear if we are going to follow Christ?

_____

_____

3.   By what one great attitude did Jesus say all men would know that we are His disciples?

_____

_____

4. There are many names used for saved people in the Bible. One such name is *soldier.* What could we learn about the Christian life simply by the term "soldier" being used as a description?

   _____

   _____

5. What are the ingredients of a good training program for the Christian soldier?

   _____

   _____

6. What types of battles do we fight in this spiritual war?

   _____

   _____

7. There is only one weapon in the Word of God for the Christian. What is it? How can we become more skilled in its use?

   _____

   _____

8. What is the primary purpose of the Church? Why should Christians serve the Lord through the ministries of a local church?

   _____

   _____

9. What is the source of power for our service to God?

   _____

   _____

10. How can we be more effective in our service to the Lord?

   _____

   _____

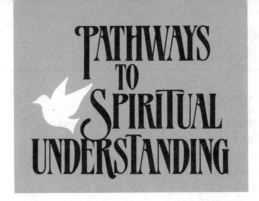

LESSON 11

The Importance of Daily Devotions

MAIN SCRIPTURES:
GENESIS 19:27; II TIMOTHY 4:7;
DANIEL 6:4-10

LESSON AIM: To lead to the conviction of the great necessity of a daily time of Bible study and prayer. To understand the value of the habit of daily devotions to your spiritual growth. To give the basic understanding of how to put together a quality quiet time with the Lord every day.

SUGGESTED MEMORY VERSES:
II Timothy 4:7; Psalm 107:1; Psalm 1:1-2; Joshua 1:8

OVERVIEW:

    I. THREE AREAS OF FITNESS IN LIFE

    II. THE PATTERN FOR DAILY DEVOTIONS

    III. PREPARATION FOR DAILY DEVOTIONS

    IV. PLAN FOR DAILY DEVOTIONS

    V. PROBLEMS OF A DAILY TIME OF DEVOTIONS

    VI. THE PURPOSE OF DAILY DEVOTIONS

INTRODUCTION: Read the story of Daniel as found in Daniel, chapter 6. When the king decreed that no one in his kingdom could make a request to any god, or offer any type of prayer for 30 days, Daniel went to God in prayer about his problem. What a great devotional life Daniel must have had! It's evident from Daniel, chapter 6 that he had a daily habit of spending time alone with God. Everyone needs to learn to do that.

The results of a recent survey showed that only approximately two out of every ten Christians have a daily time of devotions wherein they read and study God's Word and spend time in prayer.

Reports like that make it easy to understand why we have so much "spiritual anemia" among saved people. Without good devotional habits, any Christian will become weak in the faith. On the other hand, a believer who learns to invest some time daily in the Bible and in prayer will grow in faith, and will also find many spiritual blessings that others have missed.

Learn the importance of developing a good devotional habit. We need to have "family altars" where we read and study God's Word with our spouses and with our children. But before we can hope to be successful in that endeavor, we must first learn how to formulate our own personal devotional time with the Lord. This will prove to be a great blessing to your spiritual life.

(Where lines are provided after a Scripture reference, look up the verse and write a one sentence summary of what this Scripture is saying to you.)

I.   THREE AREAS OF FITNESS IN LIFE

According to the Bible, we are made in the image of God. Did you ever stop to consider what that means? Does it mean that we actually "look" like God? No. It means as God is a trinity (made of three), man was made a trinity. Learn to practice fitness in all three areas of your life. You find them listed below:

A.   God made man a ***physical*** being.

    1.   The physical part of man is the body.

        a.   We are to take care of our bodies and treat them as the "temple" of God.

        b.   I Corinthians 6:19-20 teaches that the body is the dwelling place of God.

    2.   Since the body is the dwelling place of God, we must learn to practice bodily fitness.

        a.   That of course involves a program of proper diet and exercise.

        b.   I Timothy 4:8, teaches us that there is some benefit in bodily exercise. _____

_____

_____

        c.   When the body is weak or ill we cannot function to the best of our ability for the Lord's sake. Therefore, we need to practice physical fitness to some degree.

B.   God also made man a ***mental*** being.

    1.   The mental part of man is the mind.

        a.   It is important that a Christian practice mental fitness.

        b.   As the body is affected to a great degree by what is taken in through the mouth, the mind is affected to a great degree by what is taken in through the eyes and ears.

    2.   We must take care what we put before our eyes if we are to stay mentally healthy. Psalm 101:3 _____

_____

_____

    3.   We must be careful what we listen to if we want to practice mental fitness. Proverbs 23:12 _____

_____

_____

    4.   Part of mental fitness involves proper thoughts.

        a.   Read Philippians 4:8 and list the things we are told to "think on" in this passage of Scripture. _

_____

_____

        b.   We should harbor and linger upon some

thoughts. (thoughts of praise, gratitude, faith and precious memories)

    c.   There are some thoughts which enter our mind that we must learn to cast out and refuse to think about lest they rob us of our joy and peace. *(Warning! The devil is a master at attacking us in our thought-life to discourage us.)*

C.   Finally, we learn that God made us a *spiritual* being.

    1.   To keep ourselves spiritually fit, we must learn to participate in a regular devotion time with God.

        a.   This time with God is to the spirit what food is to the body.

        b.   It provides a great source of spiritual nourishment.

II. THE PATTERN FOR DAILY DEVOTIONS

According to I Corinthians 10:11, the events of the Bible were recorded for our admonition and learning. In Genesis 19:27, Abraham sets before us an excellent example of a pattern to follow to achieve quality devotional time each day. Genesis 19:27 proves that Abraham was accustomed to meeting with the Lord on a regular basis. A pattern clearly establishes itself.

A.   Abraham got up early in the morning.

    1.   Perhaps the great sin of modern day Christianity is laziness.

        a.   We must not be afraid of the morning hours if we have a desire to draw closer to the Lord.

        b.   Psalms 5:3 _____

_____

_____

        c.   Morning hours, for many people, are less cumbered and hectic. As the day wears on and on, we have a tendency to get too busy to take the time we should with the Lord in Bible reading and prayer.

        d.   If one arose 30 minutes earlier to develop a good devotional habit, it would be a wise investment of time.

    2.   Abraham awoke with a purpose in mind.

        a.   The reason for Abraham to awaken early was to meet with the Lord. This was his purpose.

            If we are ever to be successful in our endeavor to have a regular time of devotions, we must first "purpose in our heart" that we are going to do it.

        b.   People get up early for a number of reasons.

            1.   To leave on a trip, to go on a picnic, to go fishing, to watch a certain program on T.V., to play a round of golf, to visit in the hospital, to mow the lawn, to have a

breakfast meeting, or any number of other reasons.

2. If ever there was a noble purpose for rising early in the morning it would be to meet with the Lord for some quiet time.

3. If you don't see the importance of this purpose in your life, you'll never be faithful and regular in your devotional habit.

3. Abraham did this as a daily habit.

When you read the entire context of the story, you'll realize that this was not something that Abraham did only once. Abraham had a habit of getting up early to meet with the Lord.

   a. Pray that God will help you persist in this time of meeting alone with Him so that it becomes a habit in your life.

   b. In order to develop a habit pattern, one must do the same thing, in the same way, at the same time, for 18 consecutive days. After that length of time, the activity should have become part of your daily habit pattern.

   c. Wouldn't it be worth the investment of 18 days to see if we could develop a habit of daily devotions?

B. Abraham stood before the Lord.

1. Abraham didn't rush about this business. He was patient and waited on the Lord. (Genesis 19:28)

   a. God still speaks today, but His problem with many people is getting them to sit still long enough to hear Him.

   b. We need to learn patience in our devotional life.

   c. I Thessalonians 4:11 _____

   _____

   _____

   d. We really do need to "study to be quiet," to learn how to get quiet enough to be able to hear when God is speaking to our spirit.

   e. Psalm 46:10 _____

   _____

   _____

III. PREPARATION FOR DAILY DEVOTIONS

A. First, we must prepare *internally*.

1. The first step of preparation is to yield your heart to the Holy Spirit as your teacher in God's Word. John 14:26 _____

   _____

   _____

    2.   We must also "purpose" in our heart that we are going to be faithful in our devotions.

        a.   Without determination we'll soon lose our motivation. We must have a purpose that drives us, and we must sense the importance of what we are doing.

        b.   Daniel "purposed in his heart" that he wouldn't defile himself with the king's meat and drink. We must have that same kind of internal determination that what we are doing in our daily devotion time is good for us and is right to do!

B.   We must also prepare ***externally***.

    1.   Physical preparation for devotions must begin ahead of time.

        a.   If you have yours in the morning, you need to go to bed on time and in the proper frame of mind. Late-night TV will soon destroy morning devotions.

        b.   Set your alarm to wake you early enough so that you will not be forced to rush through devotions. And when the clock goes off, give yourself time to get wide awake before you begin to seek the Lord. Don't try to lie in bed and have devotions.

    2.   If you choose to have your devotions at any other time than morning, the same type of preparations need to be made.

        You still need to be rested and prepared in such a way that you won't be tempted to rush through such an important exercise.

IV. PLAN FOR YOUR DAILY DEVOTIONS

A.   Have a specific time set aside.

    1.   Remember, when we fail to plan, we have planned to fail. Part of our plan must involve a specific time for Bible reading and prayer.

    2.   The time of day you set aside is not the great matter of importance. It may be morning, noon or night just so long as you give priority to this purpose and set aside the same time each day. It is easier to formulate a habit when using the *same time* every day.

        a.   If you give 30 minutes of your day to this cause, you will have only invested one 48th of the day.

        b.   Set aside at least 20 minutes of the day for devotions. You will receive great dividends for such a small investment.

B.   Have a specific place set aside where you meet with the Lord.

    1.   Abraham evidently had a special place. The Bible

declares that *"he gat up early...to the place where he stood before the Lord."*

2. The "place" you set aside works best if it is a private place where you are free from any outside disturbances. The devil will most certainly disturb you if he can.
    a. Your "place" needs to be free from noise and distractions.
    b. That means away from the phone, the work on your desk, the newspaper on the table, and other people.

C. Follow a specific plan every day.

The three important ingredients of a good daily devotional time are prayer, Bible reading and meditation. These will help build your spiritual life and keep you spiritually fit.

1. Begin with a brief prayer asking God to help you understand and to teach you something from His Word that will help you this very day.

2. Open your Bible and read.
    a. It helps to have a plan when you read your Bible. For instance, read three chapters of Old Testament and two chapters of New Testament everyday. Using this plan you will read through the Bible in one year and through the New Testament several times during the course of the year.
    b. You may wish to use a printed devotional guide. There are many good ones on the market.
    c. As you read, make sure that your mind isn't wandering. Be very sensitive to what the Holy Spirit may be teaching you out of the Bible.

3. Scripture memorization is also important to the Christian. Each lesson in this study recommends that you spend some time in memorizing Scripture. . This should be part of your daily devotions. Remember Psalm 119:11 _____

_____

_____

4. Spend time in prayer. In our past lesson on prayer, we learned that the secret to prayer is prayer in secret. This devotional time is your daily time of secret prayer.

5. Don't rush away after you pray. Learn to linger for a while in silence and allow the Lord to speak to your heart during this quiet time. God brings many things to mind during just such times of stillness.

V. PROBLEMS OF A DAILY TIME OF DEVOTIONS

When you decide you are going to do something that will

greatly benefit your spiritual life, you can count on some opposition from the devil. You can be certain that some problems will arise as the enemy tries to see that your daily devotions become a daily battle.

A. Concentration will be part of the battle.

1. The devil will try to steal your attention away from what your are doing.
   Refuse to let your mind get side-tracked.

2. If you resist the devil, eventually he will tire of trying to make you lose your concentration.

B. Sometimes others will unknowingly keep you from your devotions.

1. The phone will ring, someone will knock at the door, or any other number of people-related distractions will hinder you.

2. It might be necessary to change the time you had originally scheduled your devotions.

3. Putting a "please do not disturb" sign on the door helps let people know that you are having devotions.

C. Discouragement will become part of the battle.

1. No one can honestly say they have gone for a great length of time and not failed to have devotions every single day.

   a. All of us fail, and even the best of plans go astray. We must not get discouraged because we miss a day here and there.

   b. If you miss a day, don't get discouraged. Get right back to this wonderful business the next day. In so doing, you will learn how to overcome discouragement and will defeat the devil.

VI. THE PURPOSE OF DAILY DEVOTIONS

Everything we do needs to have a cause and a purpose for which we do it. There are many things that could be listed as purposes for daily devotions. We will only consider four:

A. It is fellowship with the Lord.

1. When you love someone it's only natural to have the desire to spend time with them.

2. A Christian ought to have a heartfelt desire to spend time with the Lord.

3. The only way to grow in any relationship is to invest time together. Daily devotions are a wonderful time of daily fellowship with the Lord that will build your relationship with Him.

B. Your day will be calmer because you have spent some time with the Lord.

1. Your day *will* go better when you begin it with a quiet time alone with God.

      a.   You will carry around a sense of the sweet presence of the Lord all day.

      b.   When children learn new things, we often tell them, "If you want to end right, you must make sure you get started right." Likewise, we need to take care how we start our day. Perhaps our days would end better if we started them better.

C.   Your spiritual life will grow stronger.

    1.   The Bible is to your spiritual self what the proper food is to your physical self.

    2.   A daily time of devotions to the Christian is like a daily workout to the athletic—it's good for your heart!

D.   You will be drawn into a closer walk with God.

    1.   I John 1:3 _____

            _____

            _____

    2.   According to I John 1:7 we must *"walk in the light"* if we want to enjoy closer fellowship with the Lord.

    3.   The Psalmist teaches us it is God's Word that will be a "light on our path."

    4.   Therefore, we can conclude that it is in the Bible where we meet the Lord and learn how to live pleasing to Him. This, then, is "walking in the light."

    5.   As we are drawn closer to the Lord we will learn how to be more like Jesus to others. This is the great goal of the Christian life.

SUMMARY: There are many books about physical fitness. But owning the book isn't the way to achieve fitness. One must read the book and practice what is contained therein.

Isn't that just like the spiritual life of a Christian? Many people own a Bible. But owning a Bible won't bring spiritual fitness. We must have a daily practice of reading the Bible with the purpose of practicing what we have read.

The key word to this lesson is *commitment.* In fact, that word is the key to success in any endeavor. We must learn to stay with the task. If you will commit just 20 minutes a day to devotions, you will see a great improvment in your spiritual health.

Abraham was called "the friend of God." He reached that position by entering into a close relationship with the Lord. Wouldn't it be wonderful if we walked so close to the Lord that we really felt His presence all day long? That relationship is within your reach as a child of God. In fact, it can begin tomorrow morning!

REFLECTIONS: Answer the following questions individually or in class. Give careful attention to your answers. This exercise is what the Bible refers to as *meditation.* Think on these things....

1. What is the "likeness" of God in which we are made? In what ways can we develop fitness in these areas of our lives?

   _____

   _____

2. What are some of the enemies that will endeavor to keep us from our goal of a daily time of personal devotions?

   _____

   _____

3. The Bible tells us to "study to be quiet." What does this mean to you?

   _____

   _____

4. What is the first area of "preparation" when determining to develop a good devotion habit?

   _____

   _____

5. Are there any bad places to try to have daily devotions? If so, where and why?

   _____

   _____

6. What problems can you expect to encounter in your quest for a daily quiet time with the Lord? How can you overcome them?

   _____

   _____

7. What are the key ingredients of a daily devotional time?

   _____

   _____

8. How long should your daily quiet time last?

   _____

   _____

9. What benefits and blessings can you expect to see from developing a daily devotional habit?

   _____

   _____

10. What is the key word to success in this endeavor?

    _____

    _____

LESSON 12

The Word of God

MAIN SCRIPTURES:
I PETER 1:23-25; II PETER 1:19-21;
II TIMOTHY 3:14-17; PSALM 19:7-8

LESSON AIM: To lead to the assurance that God has preserved His Word for our generation. To learn the importance of the Word of God, not only in the world but in our individual lives.

SUGGESTED MEMORY VERSES: Joshua 1:8; Isaiah 40:8; II Timothy 3:16; Hebrews 4:12

OVERVIEW:

  I. THE BIBLE IS INSPIRED BY GOD.

 II. WHAT IS THE EVIDENCE THAT WE HAVE AN INSPIRED BIBLE?

III. WHY YOU CAN HAVE CONFIDENCE IN THE BIBLE AS THE WORD OF GOD.

 IV. SUGGESTIONS ON WHAT WE SHOULD DO WITH THE BIBLE.

INTRODUCTION: Not everyone believes the Bible is the Word of God. Some are actively involved in trying to discredit the Bible and disprove its inspiration.

There comes the day that each person must study the Bible for himself and reach a personal conviction as to this wonderful book. Was it really inspired by God? Is it actually the Word of God or does it just contain the word of God? Is it a completed book? Is it a book for my generation? What's God teaching in the Bible? For what purpose did He give His Word?

The purpose of this lesson is to help you reach a deep and settled conviction as to the Bible and its value in your Christian life. The standard for all the doctrines that we have studied and will study in this series and the standard for all faith and practice within the Church is an infallible Bible. The "foundation" of our work is the Word of God.

If the Bible isn't God's holy and inspired Word, all that has been done in the ministry has been done in vain, for it has all been based and built upon the Bible as the Word of an almighty God. Therefore, you must have confidence in your Bible.

(Where lines are provided after a Scripture reference, look up the verse and write a one sentence summary of what this Scripture is saying to you.)

I. THE BIBLE IS INSPIRED BY GOD

A. II Timothy 3:16 teaches that all Scripture is inspired by God. Fill in this verse _____

_____

_____

1. What is *inspiration?*

a. The word, translated from Greek in the New Testament, is a combination of two words that literally mean. *"God breathed."*

b. It means that God gave us His Word by direct and divine dictation.

c. According to II Peter 1:21, He used many human secretaries. Even so, the words are the very words of God. Look up and write a summary of II Peter 1:21 _____

_____

_____

2. What about "verbal plenary" inspiration of the Bible?

a. *Verbal* means that every word was a word chosen carefully by God.

God didn't just plant thoughts in the minds of those men who wrote. He dictated each and every Word of the Bible to them.

b. *Plenary* simply means that inspiration is full, or complete.

1. Read Revelation 22:18-19 and write a short summary of what is taught. _____

_____

_____

2. This is a very important conviction about the Bible; for if God didn't give us a completed Bible we must leave the door open for continued revelation.

3. If we do that we, must try to determine who is really giving us a new message from God and who isn't. This would generate confusion in our churches and in our lives. I Corinthians 14:33 says that God is not the author of confusion.

4. With the Apostle John and the Book of Revelation, God finished His Word and has wondrously preserved it for our generation.

B. Why do we need an inspired Bible?

1. Because man was separated from God by sin.

a. When you read the Book of Genesis you find that when he sinned, man was separated from God.

    b.   If God and man were to be drawn together again, God first had to communicate with man.

    c.   He communicated with us through His written Word.

2.   Because God wanted to reveal His great plan for man's salvation.

    a.   Read Romans 10:13-17. You'll find that *"faith cometh by hearing, and hearing by the Word of God."*

    b.   God sent us His plan for our forgiveness and restoration. It's found in the Bible.

3.   Because God wanted to give authority to the Church.

    a.   The Word of God is the final authority for all that we believe and practice in our Churches.

    b.   Read II Timothy 3:16 again. List what the Word of God is profitable for. _____

          _____

          _____

    c.   Now read verse 17. You'll find that the Word of God is that which perfectly equips the man of God to go out and do the work of God. There is nothing lacking in the ability of the Bible!

    d.   John 12:46-48 teaches us that it is the Word of God which will someday be used as the standard of judgment for the world.

II. WHAT IS THE EVIDENCE THAT WE HAVE AN INSPIRED BIBLE?

There are many proofs of inspiration. A few are listed for your consideration.

A.   The Bible is the only book that is inexhaustible.
      You can read through the Bible many times over, and find new things each time.

    1.   It isn't that you missed portions in your previous reading. It's the fact that the Bible cannot be exhausted.

    2.   It is not uncommon to read through the Bible 25 or more times, yet find new principles and precepts with every reading. That is the wonderful inexhaustible ability of the Word of God.

B.   The Bible has been an indestructible book through many centuries.

    1.   No other writing has survived vicious attacks as has the Word of God.

        a.   It has been hated, banned, and burned, yet it still stands year after year.

        b.   Long after its enemies have passed from the scene, the Bible will still survive! Isaiah 40:8 __

_____

_____

2. Read the story of King Jehoiakim who tried to destroy God's Word in the days of Jeremiah the prophet. (You can find this story in Jeremiah, chapter 36.)
    a. What did God say to Jeremiah after King Jehoiakim had slashed and burned the Word of God upon the hearth? Jeremiah 36:28 _____

    _____

    b. King Jehoiakim found that God's Word was not easily destroyed.
    c. Think of the many centuries that have passed since God first moved man to record His word. The Bible has stood the test of time and torture.

3. Man has not yet made the first discovery that discredits the Bible.
    a. In fact, there are growing numbers of scientists today who are strong believers in the Bible as the Word of God.
    b. Other textbooks must be updated every few years, but the Bible remains as relevant today as the day in which it was written.
    c. Matthew 24:35 _____

    _____

C. The Bible is an infallible Book.

    1. There are 31,173 verses in the Bible. Each is the Word of God. Therefore, they are as infallible as God is.

    2. Read Psalm 19:7-8 and list the qualities of the "law of the Lord." _____

    _____

    3. Within the Scripture itself, the Bible is referred to as "the Word of God."
        a. This is the title used in Scripture more than any other.
        b. If the Bible is the *Word* of God, it cannot lie, for God cannot lie. Titus 1:2 _____

    _____

D. The Bible is the only book that is indispensable to the Christian's ministry.

1. There are many books that you would miss if you
   could no longer have them.
   a. These books are a help as you study your
       Bible; but these books aren't the Bible!
   b. The Bible is the only book that the Christian
       can't do without.

2. For one thing you can't be saved apart from the
   Word of God.
   a. Psalms 119:130 _____

       _____

   b. The Word of God is the "incorruptible seed"
       mentioned in I Peter 1:23 _____

       _____

       Notice, we are born again by the Word of God
       "which liveth and abideth forever."

3. Your faith can't grow apart from the Word of God.
   a. Romans 10:17 teaches that faith comes by
       hearing the Word of God.
   b. Whenever you need a "faithlift," get alone with
       your Bible. You can't help but have your faith
       increased when you read the wonderful stories
       of the heros of the faith. You will read how,
       with God's help, these great men and women
       overcame great odds and won victories that
       seemed impossible.
   c. The God of the characters in the Bible is the
       very God that we love and serve. According to
       His own Word, He doesn't change. That means
       He is able to help you overcome great odds
       today and win victories in your life, too.

4. We could not preach apart from the Word of God.
   a. The Bible must remain the central theme of
       the life of every pastor, evangelist, missionary
       and full time church worker.
   b. It is the Bible that we must preach if we want
       to see the blessing of God upon our lives and
       upon our ministries.
   c. II Timothy 4:2 _____

       _____

   d. We must preach it in all "seasons" (which
       means in all circumstances and situations).
   e. Bible preaching is part of God's plan for
       evangelization. I Corinthians 1:21 _____

       _____

       _____

5. Paul's message to Timothy (found in II Timothy 4:2)

gives the different "types" of preaching and what
God has planned that preaching to bring about in
the lives of those who are saved.

a.   List them here. _____

_____

_____

b.   We are to preach with all longsuffering and
doctrine. Often, pastors grow weary in the
ministry, give up, and quit. Determine to pray
for your pastor as He seeks to find what God
would have him preach. This isn't a easy task.
In fact, it's much more difficult than many ever
imagine. Your pastor needs your prayers and
your support in His preaching ministry.
Preaching pleases God and builds up the
saints.

III. WHY YOU CAN HAVE CONFIDENCE IN THE BIBLE AS THE WORD OF GOD

The most important part of any structure is its foundation. It
may be a beautiful building above ground, but if its
foundation isn't secure it's a worthless building.

Countless thousands of hours every week are invested
around the world in the work of God in one form or another.
We must be sure that our foundation is secure. The
foundation for the word of God is the Word of God. If the
Bible is our foundation, then our foundation is secure.

A.   The unity of the Bible is a miracle.

1.   The Bible was written by over 40 different human
"secretaries" over a period of 1600 years in two
languages.
a.   Every portion of the Bible agrees perfectly
with every other portion.
b.   Without the hand of God in its writing this
would be impossible.
c.   II Peter 1:20-21 _____

_____

_____

2.   The link between the Old Testament and the New
Testament is amazing.
a.   It has been said, "The Old Testament is the
New Testament concealed, and the New
Testament is the Old Testament revealed." This
is very true.
b.   The perfect unity between these two divisions
of the Bible is outstanding.
c.   When you read the Book of Hebrews in the
New Testament, you need to read the Book of
Leviticus in the Old Testament to arrive at the
understanding of the atonement for sins
through the shed blood of a lamb.

     d.   It takes the Book of Daniel in the Old Testament to shed light on the Book of Revelation in the New Testament.

     e.   The 53rd chapter of Isaiah in the Old Testament teaches us of the One who would be "bruised for our iniquities," and all four of the Gospels in the New Testament bear out this truth in the record of Christ Jesus.

     f.   One would never understand what Paul meant when he referred to Christ as our "Passover" in I Corinthians 5, of the New Testament, without first reading the account of the Passover in Exodus 12, of the Old Testament.

3.   It is this wonderful unity between the books of the Old Testament and the books of the New Testament, separated by hundreds of years, that builds confidence in the Bible as the Word of God.

     a.   This kind of unity would be impossible in our own day of modern communications, much less many centuries in the past when men couldn't communicate as freely with one another as we can today.

     b.   Just think—without telephones, typewriters, word processors or even printing presses, these men, "moved by God," wrote a book of perfect unity.

     c.   This book has to be the Word of God. There is no other explanation for its perfect unity.

B.   Confidence in the Bible increases when one reads of the many prophecies that have been fulfilled.

1.   If you wrote a list of predictions for this coming year and 85 out of every 100 of your predictions came to pass, you would be a wealthy man. Soon you would be heralded as a great prophet.

     a.   Yet, the Bible can claim the amazing record of 100% when it comes to accuracy in its prophecies.

     b.   Now that builds confidence!

2.   Look at this list of prophecies concerning Christ, found in the Old Testament.

     a.   Genesis 3:15—that the Messiah would be born of the seed of the woman.

     b.   Genesis 12:3—the nation through which He would be born (the Jews, or the seed of Abraham).

     c.   Genesis 49:10—from which of the twelve tribes he would come (the tribe of Judah).

     d.   II Samuel 7:12—the exact family from the tribe of Judah through which the redeemer would be born (the family of David).

     e.   Micah 5:2—town of His birth (Bethlehem).

     f.   Daniel 9:25—the exact time of His birth (483 years after the end of the time of captivity for the Jews).

      g.   Malachi 3:1—that a "forerunner" would come before Him. (This was John the Baptist.)

      h.   Zechariah 9:9—His triumphal entry into Jerusalem riding upon a colt.

      i.   Zechariah 11:12-13—His price of betrayal (30 pieces of silver).

3.   All of these prophecies about Christ were made a minimum of 400 years before His birth. Every one of these prophecies came to pass in Jesus!

      a.   Noted author Josh McDowell estimated the odds of such an event taking place by mere chance at 160 billion to 1!

      b.   The prophecies of the Bible build confidence that this Book is the very Word of God.

C.   One of the greatest proofs of the Divine inspiration of the Bible is found in its great ability to change men and transform lives!

    1.   Read Hebrews 4:12 _____

        _____

        _____

    2.   The word *quick* means alive. This Book is a living book. According to this same verse, it is also a powerful book.

      a.   The Bible has an influence upon the lives of people that no other book possesses.

      b.   Churches are filled with people whose lives have been changed by coming in contact with the Word of God.

      c.   No other book has that power, for no other book can claim to be the Word of God!

IV. SUGGESTIONS ON WHAT WE SHOULD DO WITH THE BIBLE

If you have arrived at the conviction that the Bible is the very Word of God, divinely inspired and preserved, what should you do with your Bible?

A.   Read and study it personally.

    1.   The Bible will do you no good sitting on the mantle at home. Open it and study it personally, so you might become an "approved workman" who is not ashamed.

    2.   II Timothy 2:15 _____

        _____

        _____

B.   Read it and teach it in your home with your family gathered around.

    1.   Much family strife could be resolved around a time of family devotions where the Bible is read and studied together.

2.   Read Deuteronomy 6:4-9 and you'll find the importance the Word of God has within the home.

C.   Memorize it.

Nothing will do as much good in the life of a Christian as will committing the Word of God to memory.

1.   It is this "hidden Word" that will help us in our battle with sin.

2.   Psalms 119:11 _____

_____

_____

D.   Preach it in our churches.

1.   Preaching the Word of God draws the blessing of God.

2.   And, preaching the Word of God builds us up in our faith. II Timothy 4:2 _____

_____

_____

E.   "Walk the Bible" in our daily lives.

1.   Psalm 119:105, *"Thy word is a lamp unto my feet, and a light unto my path."* The Bible guides us through difficult times and helps us face the tough decisions we all must make.

2.   We must learn to be "doers" of the Word of God and not just "hearers" only (James 1:22). _____

_____

_____

SUMMARY: In the city of London, England, there stands a tall, impressive building called the Tower of London. The British crown jewels are kept in the Tower. Also housed in that building is the "sword of state," the official sword used for many centuries in the coronation ceremony.

Bedecked with precious stones of every sort, it dazzles the eye of all who behold it.

Another "sword', however, far surpasses the "sword of state" in London. Its value is beyond earthy compare! It's the sword of the Spirit, the Word of God! Ephesians 6:17 says, *"And take the helmet of salvation, and the sword of the Spirit, which is the word of God."* This is the only weapon for the child of God. We must not lack in understanding its use, for to do so is to leave ourselves open to the attack of the enemy. With the Word of God we can fight the spiritual battle that Satan wages against us every day, and we can win!

Keep your Bible close at hand. Look to it every day. Hide it in your heart. Walk in its principles and precepts. Let its light shine on your path through life until it guides you safely home on the other side!

REFLECTIONS: Answer the following questions individually or in class. Give careful attention to your answers. This exercise is what the Bible refers to as *meditation.* Think on these things....

1. Why do we say that the Bible is the foundation for our faith and practice within the Church?

   _____

   _____

2. If the above statement is true, what convictions must we have concerning the Word of God?

   _____

   _____

3. What does "inspiration" refer to concerning the Bible?

   _____

   _____

4. List at least three proofs of inspiration.

   _____

   _____

5. Paul wrote to Timothy of the purposes for preaching the Word of God. List a few of those purposes.

   _____

   _____

6. The Bible has some amazing abilities. List those that come to your mind.

   _____

   _____

7. If the Bible truly is the "inspired and preserved Word of God," what should our attitude be toward it? What should we do with our Bibles?

   _____

   _____

8. In your opinion, what is the greatest verse "in" the Bible "about" the Bible?

   _____

   _____

The Importance of Your Testimony

MAIN SCRIPTURES:
II CORINTHIANS 5:14-21;
I TIMOTHY 4:7-12; I CORINTHIANS 9:19-27

LESSON AIM: To lead to the conviction that all those who are saved are to be "ambassadors" for Christ upon the earth. To help understand the importance of having a good testimony before others. To lead to the understanding that we bear not only our own reputation but also the reputation of Christ Jesus.

SUGGESTED MEMORY VERSES:
Proverb 22:1; Galatians 5:16; Matthew 5:16; I Timothy 4:12; Philippians 1:27

OVERVIEW:

   I. EVERY CHRISTIAN IS CALLED TO BE THE LORD'S AMBASSADOR

   II. THE AMBASSADOR'S LIFE OF EXAMPLES

   III. THE MOST DIFFICULT DUTY OF THE CHRISTIAN AMBASSADOR

INTRODUCTION: Proverbs 22:1 is a wonderful verse with a tremendous Bible principle to teach every child of God. That verse says, *"A good name is rather to be chosen than great riches, and loving favor rather than silver and gold."* A good definition of the word *reputation* is, "the public estimation of one's nature and character." In other words, your reputation is what people say about you when you aren't around to hear. And that happens to all of us whether we are aware of those conversations or not.

For the Christian, a better word than reputation may be the word *testimony*. Your testimony is one of the most important facets of your Christian life. Proverbs 22:1 teaches that our testimony should be more valuable to us than silver, gold and great wealth. It takes only a few moments to destroy a reputation or testimony that may have taken many years to build. Once lost, it's very difficult to regain our testimony before others. Therefore, we must learn the great value of our testimony, and we must learn how to develop it into a *"good name that is rather to be chosen than great riches."* We also have the duty to learn how to protect our testimony. We who are saved carry not only our own name; we also bear the name of Christ before the world. This is a great responsibility summed up in the words of the Apostle Paul, *"Now then we are ambassadors for Christ."*

(Where lines are provided after a Scripture reference, look up the verse and write a one sentence summary of what this Scripture is saying to you.)

I. EVERY CHRISTIAN IS CALLED TO BE THE LORD'S AMBASSADOR

Read II Corinthians 5:17-21. The Bible says that believers are ambassadors for Christ on the earth. Every Christian, every day, in every place, is moving under Divine orders! It's vital, therefore, that we understand our obligation in this business of representing our Lord before others.

A. The meaning of the term, *ambassador*.

    1. An ambassador is an envoy of the highest rank, sent by a sovereign ruler to be his representative to another nation or another people.

        As ambassadors of Christ, we have been commissioned to serve God here upon the earth and to bear His name before others.

    2. We must remember that, even though we live in this world, this world isn't our home.

        a. We who are saved have citizenship in Heaven.

        b. Colossians 3:2 _____

          _____

          _____

        c. We who are the Lord's ambassadors ought not set our heart and affection upon the things of this world. When compared to eternity, we won't live here very long.

    3. The ambassador may be called home at any time by his ruling power.

        a. We are told this truth in the Bible.

          Proverb 27:1 _____

          _____

          _____

        b. Our life is very uncertain, and we must make the most of every opportunity to be a good representative of our Lord to others.

B. The mission of the ambassador.

    1. The whole mission of an ambassador can be summed up this way: He goes to all places, to all people, at all times and in all circumstances.

        a. A good ambassador goes wherever he is sent.

        b. He goes cheerfully and willingly.

    2. The Lord sent His ambassadors into the world to carry the good news of the gospel to others so they could be saved.

        a. We know from the Bible that "the field" is the world.

        b. We can't go to the wrong place. Everywhere we go, we'll find those who need Christ in their lives.

        c. We, as the ambassadors of Christ, must be willing to go wherever He sends us.

     d.   A good ambassador is the one who is content with his station in life. He doesn't complain about his mission; he serves to the very best of his ability.

     e.   We haven't all been given the same mission. The work of the Lord couldn't get done if that were the case. We ought not envy the position that our Lord has assigned to others. He has placed us where He wants us; this should cause us to be content.

     f.   Let each of us fill his or her post with joy and contentment.

C.   The manners of an ambassador.

    1.   An ambassador is required to behave himself in a manner that won't bring shame upon his ruler.

       a.   The similarity isn't too difficult for us to see in the life of a Christian ambassador.

       b.   All that we say or do reflects upon the One who saved us. Therefore, we must remember to carry the manners of a good ambassador.

    2.   The ambassador's dress should reflect the proper message to others.

       a.   We who are saved needn't worry about keeping up with all the latest styles and being a walking fashion show; we should dress according to the Bible's admonition.

       b.   I Timothy 2:9 _____

_____

_____

           This Scripture doesn't forbid all make-up or jewelry, but rather, is an admonition to modesty in dress.

       c.   A Christian ought not dress in a flashy manner solely for the purpose of calling attention to himself.

       d.   In many cases today, the unsaved are "turned off" by Christians who display an overabundance of extremes in their style of dress. We must remember that we are ambassadors of Christ, and the world needs to see Jesus in us.

       e.   Likewise, it's wrong to dress in meager fashion just to display a sense of humility or some false sense of piety. We must learn to allow the Holy Spirit to guide us by His convicting power, even in the area of our "outward adorning."

    3.   Not only should the ambassador's dress be a good testimony for the Lord, but the ambassador's demeanor must also bring glory to God.

       a.   Your demeanor is your temperament and your attitudes.

    b.   Many Christians need to work more on their "inward" adorning than they do on their outward adorning.

    c.   I Corinthians 6:20 teaches us that we are to glorify God in our spirit, or our temperament, and attitudes.

    d.   God looks upon our hearts today. What does He see when He looks within our lives?

    e.   Many try to make excuses for their ill spirit and unpleasant demeanor by saying, "That's just the way I am." They forget however, the Holy Spirit lives within to change them into what the Lord wants them to be. To resign yourself to live with less than a Christ-honoring temperament is to deny the power of the Holy Spirit at work in your life.

    f.   A good ambassador will consistently display the grace and character of Christlikeness. It may not always be easy, but it is always our duty!

D.   The message of the Lord's ambassador.

    1.   Every good ambassador carries the message he has been given by his commander. One of his greatest duties is to communicate this message properly and clearly.

    2.   Sometimes our message as the Lord's ambassadors is one of *reconciliation.*

        a.   We who are saved need to be in the business of helping restore those who have stumbled and fallen in their faith.

        b.   There are many who are casualities of the devil and need a friend to help them in the area of reconciliation.

        c.   Our orders are found in Galatians 6:1 _____

        _____

        _____

        d.   Notice the spirit we must carry when we engage in this great work is the spirit of meekness.

        e.   Someone you know is just waiting for a good ambassador to come along and bring him the message of reconciliation in the spirit of meekness.

    3.   Sometimes the message we must carry is the message of *salvation.*

        a.   This message demands our urgent attention, for life is uncertain and many are dying without Christ as their Savior!

        b.   We need to keep the message of salvation uncomplicated. We must make it clear and simple.

        c.   The message of salvation is unconfined. The

Lord has invited "whosoever will" to be saved.
Romans 10:13 _____

_____

_____

d.   The message of salvation is unconditional.
There is no one that cannot be saved! The
Bible teaches that Jesus is able to save, even
the "uttermost" sinner. Hebrews 7:25 _____

_____

_____

e.   A good ambassador of Christ will take every
opportunity to share his wonderful message
with others. Remember, the gospel has never
gone where someone didn't take it.

II. THE AMBASSADOR'S LIFE OF EXAMPLES

Read I Timothy 4:7-12. As found in this passage of Scripture,
there are at least six important areas in which we are to be
living examples before others:

A.   The ambassador is to be an example in *word*.

    1.   Even the words that come out of our mouths are to
be a proper example of Christianity.
       a.   Psalm 19:14 _____

_____

_____

       b.   This Psalm ought to be memorized by every
Christian who is concerned about being a
good example for Christ.

    2.   According to Matthew 12:34 there's a direct link
between the heart and the mouth.
       a.   When our mouth doesn't speak rightly, it's a
good indicator that our heart isn't right with
God.
       b.   Ephesians 4:29 _____

_____

_____

Any communication that is curt, cold, cruel,
cutting, critical or caustic is corrupt!
       c.   Let your words be a good testimony to others.

B.   The ambassador is to be an example in *conversation*.

    1.   This isn't the same as in "word." Here, the word
"conversation" refers to daily life that others see.
       a.   It means your daily lifestyle is to be a good
testimony.
       b.   Philippians 1:27 _____

_____

_____

2. The only way any one can live this kind of Christ-honoring life day by day is to learn how to live life in the power of the Holy Spirit.

    It's the power of God that tranforms us into a good testimony before others. And by His power we can be an example in our daily behavior.

C. The ambassador is to be an example in ***charity***.

    1. The word *"charity"*, translated here, is love.
        a. God's people ought to be an example in the love they have for others.

    2. This love is to be the distinguishing mark of our faith! John 13:35 _____

        _____

        _____

    3. One of the best word-studies you can do with your Bible is to study every verse that mentions the word *"love."*
        a. I Thessalonians 4:9 _____

            _____

            _____

        b. Also look at I Peter 1:22 and I John 4:11.
        c. We should love the Lord first, others second, and self last. But how often do we get that priority backwards? May God help us today to be examples in our love.

D. The ambassador is to be an example in ***spirit***.

    1. We have already touched on this area briefly. It refers to our attitudes—or to use a word easily understood by everyone today, *"moods."*
        a. Even your moods ought to be brought into subjection.
        b. Ephesians 4:30-32 teaches more about the proper attitudes of a good ambassador.
        c. When you read Ephesians 4:30-32, what do you find in the "negative" areas that you ought to put away from yourself? _____

            _____

            _____

        d. What positive attitudes should your spirit display? _____

            _____

            _____

E. The ambassador is to be an example in *faith*.

    1. For an excellent definition of faith, you must read Hebrews 11:1.
        a. You'll find that real faith is trusting God even in the times when you cannot "see" how He is

going to be able to come through!

    b.   Faith isn't something you must be able to see or handle before you believe.

    c.   Faith is taking God's Word as all the evidence you need!

  2. If you read all of Hebrews, chapter 11, you'll read the stories of those who were heros of the faith and lived so as to be good ambassadors by their faith in God.

    a.   We need to live our faith before others even in the times of trial or adversity. This is when our faith becomes a real example to others. Faith that is genuine is only strengthened and improved by adversity.

F.   The ambassador is to be an example in *purity.*

  1. In a day when so very many live less than pure lives, we who name the name of Christ must live the lifestyle of purity to bring honor to our Lord. The world will soon despise the professed Christian who doesn't live any differently than those who don't profess to be saved.

  2. If you read the story of Lot in Genesis 19, you'll find a classic example of this principle.

    a.   The men of Sodom mocked Lot (verse 9) because he lived just as they lived and then attempted to condemn their actions.

    b.   We who are ambassadors for Christ must make sure the world doesn't have good reason to mock us because of our lack of consistency.

    c.   The world may not appreciate the morals of the Christian, but let them not despise us for the lack of moral purity.

    d.   As the Lord's ambassadors, we must work and serve Him "in" the world but we must not allow the morals of the world to influence the way we behave and the way we live. Let us always remember we have been called to be an example of purity.

III. THE MOST DIFFICULT DUTY OF THE CHRISTIAN AMBASSADOR

As ambassadors for Christ, we often face difficult tasks. But the most difficult isn't fighting the world, the cults, the humanist or even the devil. The most difficult duty is that of keeping the flesh disciplined.

The sign of maturity is self-discipline. For instance, the more children learn to discipline themselves, the less they need their parents involvement in the control of their behavior.

Surely it must please our Heavenly Father when we grow in the area of self-discipline. It's a certain sign of "spiritual maturity" in our lives. It may not always be easy to control the flesh and to discipline self, but it is always right, and it is beneficial to our character and testimony before the world.

There are four primary areas of life that we must learn to discipline ourselves in if we are to live a good testimony before others.

A.   We must discipline our *devotions.*

1.   We've already devoted an entire chapter to this important area of our lives, but let us be reminded that we MUST have a daily, quiet time of personal and private devotions, alone with the Lord, if we are to maintain our spiritual health.

   a.   There is no way for our spirit to grow without good spiritual nourishment.

   b.   I Peter 2:2 _____

   _____

   _____

2.   We must remember that Jesus is a person, and we need to walk in a close relationship with Him.

   a.   We need to seek Him in the first part of our day. Proverbs 8:17 _____

   _____

   _____

   b.   If we are to be His ambassador, we must know Him and walk with Him. How can we be a representative of Him whom we do not know?

3.   The two primary ingredients of a good devotional time are prayer, and the Word of God.

   a.   In the Word of God we hear from God; in our prayer time we speak with Him directly!

   b.   Daily discipline in this area of life will pay off in a closer relationship with the Lord Jesus.

B.   We must discipline our *doubts.*

1.   Some people harbor doubts and negative attitudes constantly.

   a.   A doubting Christian will be a discouraged Christian, and a discouraged Christian will soon be a defeated Christian.

   b.   This is no way for the Lord's ambassador to live!

2.   To avoid the snare of discouragement, one must learn to discipline a doubting mind.

   a.   The first step is to avoid those who are, themselves, undisciplined in this area.

   b.   It only took 10 defeated, negative spies to keep all of God's people out of the Land of Canaan. Surround yourself with people who are always discouraged and defeated, and their attitude will "rub off" on you.

   c.   You must learn to practice controlling your thoughts. According to the Bible, you can accomplish this with God's help.

II Corinthians 10:5 _____

_____

_____

d. God made our minds in such manner that we cannot possibly think two different thoughts at the exact same time. Therefore, we must learn to "cast out" the negative, hindering thoughts by replacing them with that which is good. By persisting in this exercise, you will learn to control your mind and direct its thoughts.

C. We must learn to discipline our **desires.**

1. Salvation doesn't destroy our old nature. We must understand that the *"flesh"* (the old nature) will battle the *"spirit"* (which is the new nature given to us by the indwelling Spirit of God).

    a. If we're to live a good testimony, we must learn to disciple and control the flesh along with its desires.

2. According to I John 2:16, these desires fall into three main categories. Read this passage and list the three categories. _____

    _____

    _____

    a. The lust of the flesh deals with things like sensual desires and love of pleasure.

    b. The lust of the eyes deals with the desire to accumulate more and more of the world's wealth—materialism!

    c. The pride of life is to have a haughty spirit—to desire the praise of men and to want to be popular in the eyes of the world.

3. To discipline these areas of life we must learn to resist at the point of temptation or desire. This is where all sin finds it's beginning.

    a. Read James 1:13-15. It's at the moment of enticement that we must learn to resist in the power of God.

    b. Each time a Christian stands up and resists at the moment of enticement or temptation, he or she grows stronger for the next attack of temptation by this particular sin. If he continues to resist, the victory over that sin will come.

    c. The devil cannot *make* you sin; he can only lead you to the point where you will be enticed. Even that comes from your own lust (flesh), according to James, chapter 1.

D. We must learn to discipline our **duties.**

1. The word *"duty"* is the word that separates the

good Christian from the average Christian.

a. Read and copy Ecclesiastes 12:13. _____

_____

_____

b. The Christian's whole duty to God is to fear (reverence) Him and to keep His commandments.

2. The undisciplined Christian is motivated to serve the Lord out of "inspiration."

a. If you can keep him inspired, you can keep him serving the Lord and being a good ambassador.

b. The only problem with this motivation is that inspiration often runs out! It's extremely difficult to always keep people inspired.

3. The disciplined Christian is the one who serves not out of inspiration, but out of obligation.

a. He sees his service to the Lord as a soldier sees his service to his country. It's his duty!

b. He is a child of God. He represents the Lord before the world, He is His ambassador. It is his duty and obligation to keep his testimony clean and to serve God even when he doesn't feel inspired!

c. Whatever God has commanded in His Word, that is what he will do...for he is an ambassador of Christ.

SUMMARY: Of all the people who have ever lived since Adam was created and placed here, upon this earth, very few ever had the privilege to physically meet the Lord Jesus face to face. He lived in a very confined area of the world for a very short period of time. The millions of people in the world today will never see Jesus if they don't see Him in those of us who are saved. That's why the Bible says, *"Now then we are ambassadors for Christ...."* He left us here in His place to represent Him before others. That's the duty of every saved man, woman, teenager, boy or girl.

It's vital that we understand the importance of our testimony, and our duty to guard it carefully. Many times a testimony that has taken years to build only takes minutes to destroy. This thought should so guide us each day that we may learn how to resist the attacks of the devil and protect our valuable testimony.

Did people see Jesus in you this week? Did they see Him in your life? "Show Him" to others by the way you live, the places you go, the things you do, the attitudes you display and the words you say. This is the duty of a good ambassador!

REFLECTIONS: Answer the following questions individually or in class. Give careful attention to your anwers, this exercise is what the Bible refers to as *meditation.* Think on these things....

1. The Bible is careful in it's use of every word and every term.

Why then is the word "ambassador" a good term for the life of a Christian?

_____

_____

2. In one sentence, sum up the duty of an ambassador.

_____

_____

3. Is it proper for an ambassador to train himself in things related to character and manners? How does this relate to the Christian ambassador?

_____

_____

4. In what areas of life did the Apostle Paul tell Timothy he was to be an example of the Believers? As you list them, pray about the areas of your life where you need to allow the Holy Spirit to teach you how to be a better example.

_____

_____

5. Matthew 12:34 teaches there is a direct link between our _____ and our _____. Fill in the blanks and explain this principle in one or two sentences.

_____

_____

6. What is, perhaps, the most difficult task of the Christian ambassador?

_____

_____

7. What areas of life must we learn to discipline if we are to carry a good testimony before the world?

_____

_____

8. What does it mean to be motivated by inspiration?

_____

_____

9. What does it mean to be motivated by obligation?

_____

_____

10. Read II Corinthians 4:11. Pay special attention to the last part of the verse. What does this verse teach?

_____

_____

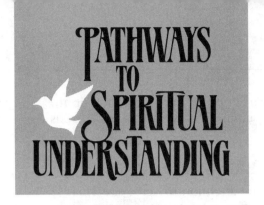

PATHWAYS TO SPIRITUAL UNDERSTANDING

LESSON 14

Witnessing

MAIN SCRIPTURES:
PSALM 126; ACTS 8:26-40; LUKE 15:1-11
JOHN 1:35-42

LESSON AIM: To learn, from Scripture, the importance of bringing others to Christ. To learn how to use the Word of God effectively in witnessing. To gain confidence and encouragement in telling others the Gospel.

SUGGESTED MEMORY VERSES:
Proverbs 11:30; Romans 3:23; Romans 5:8; Romans 6:23; Romans 10:9-10; Romans 10:13

OVERVIEW:

    I. THE BUSINESS THAT BRINGS BLESSINGS

  11. LESSONS FROM THE MAN WHO BROUGHT HIS BROTHER TO JESUS

  III. BIBLE EXAMPLES IN HOW TO WIN OTHERS TO CHRIST

  IV. THREE SIMPLE STEPS TO WINNING SOMEONE TO CHRIST BEFORE THE YEAR IS OVER

INTRODUCTION: The most important day in your life was the day you trusted Christ Jesus as your own personal Savior. That day forever changed your life both here and in eternity. The full significance of that decision will not be realized until you live your last day on earth and then cross from this life into the next life in Heaven. Of all the decisions you have made, this one is the most vital!

The most important work in all the world is bringing others to Christ. This is the work that Jesus, Himself, came to do, for He said He came to *"seek and to save that which is lost."* It is the business He has given those who are saved. The reason there are so many problems in so many churches is we don't center our ministries and our lives on witnessing and winning the lost to Christ.

It always creates a sweet spirit in the church when the main business is the business of spreading the Gospel and winning the lost. This is a work every saved person can do whether man, woman, teenager, boy or girl. It doesn't take a degree in theology to witness and win the lost; it only takes a desire, a burden, and a simple knowledge of the Scripture, along with total reliance upon the help of the Holy Spirit. If you are saved you can tell others how to be saved. It only becomes difficult when the devil fools us into believing it's difficult. Eighty percent of all Christians never witness to anyone about their faith before they die.

In this lesson you will learn how to use the Bible and tell others how to know Christ as their Savior. This study can only lead to the knowledge; you must supply the compassion and the burden. If you do your part, the Holy Spirit will do His part and supply you with the power to become an effective witness for Christ Jesus.

133

(Where lines are provided after a Scripture reference, look up the verse and write a one sentence summary of what this Scripture is saying to you.)

I. THE BUSINESS THAT BRINGS BLESSINGS

Read Psalm 126. Pay careful attention to verse six. This simple, yet profound verse, offers a tremendous outline and formula for witnessing to and winning the lost.

A. *"He that goeth forth...."*

1. There is no better plan for evangelism.
   a. The very first step is going out looking for those to whom we can witness.
   b. Many never witness because they never take the time to "go out" and seek.
   c. We cannot win the lost from our den or family room. We must set aside some time to go out and seek.
   d. Perhaps your church has some type of visitation or evangelism program. If so, this is the ideal place to begin.
   e. Even if you don't have an organized program of evangelism you can find those in your own circle of acquaintances who need the Gospel. It would be a wonderful place to start.

2. The command is never for the lost (unsaved) to go find a church and hear the Gospel. The command is always for the saved to go out and find those who need to be saved and tell them the good news of salvation.

3. We are told to go out quickly! Why?
   a. Luke 14:23 _____

   _____

   _____

   b. Time is short. John 9:4 _____

   _____

   _____

   c. Opportunities pass quickly. Some people only cross your path once. If the Lord opens the door to witness, seize the opportunity before it's gone forever.
   d. Life is uncertain and those to whom you should witness today may not be here tomorrow.
   e. Urgency demands that Christians get involved in witnessing and keep it foremost in church ministries.
      1. People die at an alarming rate.
      2. On the average day 160,000 people somewhere in the world go out into eternity.

       3.   Most of them are without Christ!

B.   *"And Weepeth...."*

    1.   One thing wrong in churches today is that we seem to have lost a portion of our compassion.

        a.   Many hearts have grown cold and unconcerned over the sad condition of those who are lost.

        b.   We need the "tears" back in our lives once again.

    2.   The excuses are many:

        a.   "Times have changed."

        b.   "The lost are harder to win to Christ today."

        c.   "The days that we live in are more wicked than the days our forerunners lived in."

        d.   "People are too saturated with the gospel today."

    3.   Could it truthfully be that we are so entangled with the concerns of the world around us that we Christians have grown too busy to have a burden and compassion for the lost?

        a.   The devil's great trick on this generation is "busy-ness."

        b.   Christians are too busy to read the Bible, too busy to pray, too busy to attend church, too busy to get involved in any ministry, too busy to learn and many times, too busy to take the time to witness to others.

        c.   If our excuse is "too busy," then we must sit down with our priority list and find some time to become a personal evangelist. There is no other business as important.

    4.   Our Lord certainly knew what it was to shed tears of compassion and concern over the lost.

        a.   Luke 19:41 _____

        _____

        _____

        b.   How many Christians have never shed a tear over someone they know and love who needs to be born again?

        c.   Ask the Lord to place a real burden in your heart that will lead to compassion for the condition of those without Christ.

C.   *"Bearing precious seed...."*

    1.   The *"precious seed"* is none other than the Word of God.

        a.   I Peter 1:23 _____

        _____

        _____

        b.   As we go out to witness, we must carry with

us the Word of God, for it is the incorruptible seed.

2. Read the parable of the sower, the seed, and the soil as found in Mark 4:3-20. The spiritual lessons are easy to find.

    a. The sower went out to sow. (That includes those of us who have a desire to witness to others)

    b. Notice the purpose for going out was to sow.

        1. Not to talk about the weather, sports or current events.

        2. Sometimes when we go out to witness to others we never get around to the topic we went to discuss.

    c. The seed represents the Word of God. Mark 4:14 _____

        _____

        _____

    d. The sower did not have 100 percent success in his sowing; neither will we. However, he did have some success, and we will realize enough success to make the time and effort worthwhile if we engage in the same business.

    e. Some seed fell upon "the wayside." Jesus said this represents the type of person who hears the Gospel and ignores it.

    f. Some seed fell upon "stony ground." Jesus said this represents one who has a heart that is hardened against the Gospel.

    g. Some seed fell upon "thorns." The Lord told us this represents the person who is too busy and too wrapped up in the material things of the world to care about his soul.

    h. Some seed fell upon good ground and brought forth fruit. Not everybody who hears the Gospel is going to trust Christ and be saved, but enough will be saved to teach us the importance of witnessing to others.

    i. But no "fruit" would have grown if the sower hadn't first gone out to sow the seed. What does that tell you? _____

        _____

        _____

D. *"Shall doubtless come again with rejoicing...."*

1. Here is God's promise of blessings for those who invest time in this business.

2. Lives have been changed and homes have been salvaged because somebody witnessed to others about their need to be saved. Who in your circle of family or friends is in need of the life-changing salvation that comes through knowing Christ Jesus?

Think what a blessing is in store for those who will witness to and win someone to Christ!

II. LESSONS FROM THE MAN WHO BROUGHT HIS BROTHER TO JESUS

Read John 1:35-42. In this chapter of the Bible we meet a man named Andrew who was able to bring his own brother (Simon Peter) to Jesus. The simple steps he used to bring Simon to Christ will help each of us in our endeavors to witness to others—if we follow them carefully.

A.   Andrew thought of his brother.

    1.   This may sound very basic, but the truth is, this is the first step in becoming an effective witness.

        a.   Before Andrew could bring his brother to Jesus, he had to think of him and of his need.

        b.   All actions are born out attitudes and thoughts.

        c.   "Right attitudes" equal "right actions."

        d.   Before we can ever be effective in witnessing to others, we must learn to "think" of those who are lost.

        e.   The term to remember is "soul conscience." This means that we must remember to think of those around us as people who have an eternal soul which must spend eternity in only one of two places—Heaven or Hell.

        f.   We will never be effective in witnessing until we learn to think of others.

    2.   All people without Christ are lost.

        a.   The good, the moral, the religious, the honest, the upright, the young and the old are lost without Him.

        b.   Many Christians have the mistaken idea that only the obviously sinful people are lost and need to be saved. This dangerous misconception keeps us from witnessing to others all around us who need to hear the Gospel and be saved.

B.   After he thought of his brother, Andrew sought him.

    1.   Notice John 1:41. The first few words of this verse tell us, *"He first findeth his own brother Simon...."*

        a.   Andrew got up, went out, and actively got involved in looking for Simon.

        b.   Don't ever forget that there will never be a substitute for the "go" in the "gospel."

        c.   After we think of someone we know who is lost and needs Christ, we must take the next step and seek him and do whatever we can to bring him to Christ.

    2.   Phillip is another example of a man who went seeking the lost. (Acts, chapter 8.)

        a.   Phillip didn't think it enough to just pray for the salvation of the residents of Samaria; he sought them and preached to them. Acts 8:5 __

_____

_____

    b.   All Christians need to do the same thing.

    c.   God may call some to go across the waters as a missionaries.

    d.   He may send others across the states as pastors or evangelists.

    e.   But all of us have been "sent" to those around us. It's our duty to think of them, to pray for them and to witness to them as the Holy Spirit leads and opens doors.

C.   After Andrew found Simon, he taught him.

    1.   He told Simon that he had found the Messiah.

       a.   John 1:41 _____

_____

_____

       b.   He taught Simon that Jesus was the Christ of the Old Testament. He taught him who Jesus was and what He had come to do.

       c.   That is the message of every soul-winner.

    2.   This message needs to come across to others by the way we live.

       a.   The so-called "lifestyle evangelism" we hear so much about today is certainly nothing new. Those who are saved have always been taught (in the Bible) that their lives should reflect Christ to the lost world.

       b.   What we say will never be received by the lost unless it's backed up by the way we live.

       c.   We are ambassadors for Christ. We're to represent Him before others everyday.

    3.   If we're to be effective in witnessing to others, we mustn't limit the message of Christ just to our lifestyle. The message of Christ must also be carried to others by our words.

       a.   Andrew *told* Simon about the Savior.

       b.   That's what we need to learn to do, also. The message of salvation needs to be given verbally.

       c.   Everyone needs to know how to use the Scriptures and tell others how to know Christ as their Savior.

       d.   If you are unsure of your ability to tell others how to be saved, set this as your next goal— learn the Scriptures and commit them to memory, where you'll never misplace them.

D.   Andrew thought of his brother, sought his brother, taught him about the Messiah and finally, brought him to Jesus.

1. John 1:42 tells us that Andrew brought his brother Simon to Christ.
    a. This is the most important goal for all who are witnessing to someone.
    b. Don't ever give up on anyone without reaching this wonderful goal.

2. Consider what a great thing Andrew did for Simon by bringing him to Christ.
    a. He brought him into a new life. And there is no better life to be lived that the life of one who is saved.
    b. He brought him to new associations. He is now associated with Christ and with those who are His followers. (You will never have any closer friends than your Christian friends.)
    c. He brought him to a new vocation. Peter the fisherman soon became Peter the great disciple and preacher. (It was Peter who preached on the day of Pentecost when 3,000 trusted Christ.)
    d. All of these wonderful changes came because Andrew loved his brother enough to go find him and to bring him to Jesus. Shouldn't we find joy in doing the same thing for others?

III. BIBLE EXAMPLES IN HOW TO WIN OTHERS TO CHRIST

Proverb 11:30 tells us, *"He that winneth souls is wise."* There is great wisdom in witnessing of Christ before others. It truly is the business that brings blessings. The Bible is filled with many wonderful, true accounts of faithful soul-winners who brought people to a saving knowledge of Christ Jesus. Their stories are recorded for our benefit.

A. Andrew teaches us how to win others by our love.

1. We have just studied the account of Andrew bringing his brother, Simon, to Jesus. The lesson here is that it was love that motivated him.
    a. Look, first to those you love and see if any are yet without Christ.
    b. Love ought to motivate us to witness to the lost. II Corinthians 5:14 _____

    _____

    _____

2. What a contrast Andrew is to Cain who asked the Lord, *"Am I my brother's keeper?"*

B. Phillip teaches us to witness to and win the lost by obedience.

1. Read Acts 8:27-40. Phillip's obedience played a major role in the conversion of the Ethiopian.

2. Phillip obeyed the Lord's leading and found a man whose heart was tender and who was just waiting

for someone to teach him about Christ.

3.   There are many more just like this man in the world all around us today.

4.   God expects all of us who are saved to be a witness at sometime. When the Holy Spirit convicts you to speak to someone about the Lord and you do not, you have been disobedient to the Lord.

5.   Learn to "listen" to that still, small voice inside and then be obedient in witnessing when He leads.

C. Peter teaches us to witness with confidence in the Holy Spirit.

   1.   Read the story of Peter leading Cornelius and many of his relatives to Christ as it is found in Acts 10:1-48.

      a.   Peter didn't really want to go to the house of Cornelius.

      b.   Peter was still hanging on to a little of the Jewish law and was unwilling to enter the house of a Gentile. Evidently, he had never done so before.

      c.   In Acts 10:20, the Holy Spirit tells Peter to go with the three men Cornelius sent to find him and to doubt nothing.

   2.   We must learn to trust the leadership of the Holy Spirit when we witness to others.

      a.   It's the Holy Spirit's job to lead us, empower us and teach us.

      b.   The Christian never witnesses alone. He has the constant and abiding presence of the Holy Spirit to accompany him.

      c.   It's vital that we learn to lean upon Him and trust Him as we witness to others.

         1.   Many Christians have believed the devil's lie that they don't have what it takes to witness to someone and lead that person to Christ.

         2.   If you are saved you have the Holy Spirit living within.

         3.   His presence in your life guarantees that you have what it takes to become an effective witness.

D. Paul teaches us how to win others by continuance.

   1.   Acts 26:22 _____

_____

_____

      a.   The apostle Paul "continued" witnessing.

      b.   He suffered shipwreck, imprisonment, beatings, cursings and many other dangers, yet he continued to tell others the Gospel!

      c.   The lesson here is faithfulness. Don't ever give up. Many people are won to Christ only after years of prayer and witnessing.

    d.   We must have an "unstoppable" spirit if we are to be successful in winning others to Christ. We must not be pushy or arrogant in our witness, but neither must we give up on others too easily.

IV. THREE SIMPLE STEPS TO WINNING SOMEONE TO CHRIST BEFORE THE YEAR IS OVER!

Everyone ought to learn to set goals for their lives. Some should be short-range goals and some should be long-range goals. Too many people today set all their goals in the material realm only. They set goals to build bank accounts or to pay-off our debts. While there's nothing wrong with setting these kinds of goals, there is a realm to life other than the material—the spiritual realm.

We need to set spiritual goals for ourselves every year. (One such goal would be to win at least one other person to Christ every year.) But setting goals is useless unless we also have a plan to reach our goals. The last part of this lesson is designed to help you in your goal to win others to Christ.

Read the story of Phillip, a deacon in the church of Jerusalem, found in Acts, chapter 8. Phillip went to Samaria to preach Christ to the lost in that village. He was having great success when the Lord told him to go out into the desert to wait for one man who would come riding by who needed to be saved.

Don't ever neglect the importance of one person. If there had only been one sinner in all the world, Jesus would still have come to die for that sinner. That's how important one soul is to God.

A.   Phillip was a willing worker.

    1.   Phillip was available to the Lord.
        a.   You and I must learn to be available to the Lord if we are to win others.
        b.   Too many people today are too busy in other things that will not make any eternal difference in the lives of others.
        c.   Ask yourself this question, "What on earth am I doing for Heaven's sake?" What *are* you doing that will make an eternal difference?

    2.   Acts 8:26 shows the Lord's call to Phillip, and Acts 8:27 gives Phillip's response.
        a.   No excuses were made to God as to why later would be a better time to leave Samaria. Phillip simply got up and went out. He was totally available to the Lord at any time, on any day.
        b.   If he had made any excuse at all, or if he had delayed his leaving, he would have missed his opportunity to witness to the Ethiopian.
        c.   The Ethiopian's chariot was passing by at a specific time and in a specific place. Phillip

was in the right place at the right time to win this man to Christ.

    d.   We may miss many opportunities because we are not always available to the Lord.

B.   Phillip trusted the witnessing Spirit to lead him.

    1.   We will never be very effective in witnessing to others unless we, too, learn to rely upon the help and power of the Holy Spirit. There is no substitute for the power of the Holy Spirit in our lives. Zechariah 4:6 _____

_____

_____

    2.   We can look nice, smell nice, act nice and have it all right on the outside, but without the power of the Holy Spirit on the inside, we will be fruitless.

    3.   We must know what it is to be yielded to the Holy Spirit if we are going to be effective in our witness to others.

C.   Phillip had a working knowledge of the Scriptures.

    1.   In Acts 8:35 we find that Phillip opened the Scriptures to the Book of Isaiah and preached Christ to the Ethiopian from these Scriptures.

        He couldn't have done this unless he had studied and had prior knowledge of the Word of God.

    2.   You and I need the same knowledge before we will be able to lead others to Christ.

        The soul-winner's message will be his most valuable tool. This message isn't complex, in fact it's quite simple.

D.   You will need to know the following steps and Scriptures in order to lead someone to Christ!

    1.   First, prove that the one to whom you are witnessing is a sinner and needs to be saved. You can never lead someone to Christ who is not first convinced that he is lost and needs a Savior.

        a.   Romans 3:10 _____

_____

_____

        Romans 3:23 _____

_____

_____

        b.   Using these two verses you can prove from the Bible that everyone is a sinner, therefore everyone needs a Savior.

    2.   Second, show the wages of sin (or the fact that there is a price connected to sin).

        a.   Romans 6:23. _____

_____

b. The first part of this verse shows, from the Bible, that the wage of sin is death. Point out that to die without Christ is to die lost and hopeless. The only alternative to salvation is to spend eternity in the place the Bible calls Hell.

3. Show that Jesus died to pay the sin-debt of the one to whom you are witnessing.

   a. Romans 5:8 _____

   _____

   _____

   b. Point out that Christ died "for" us. (He died to pay our sin debt!)
      1. He died that we might live eternally.
      2. Some believe that since Christ died for us already, we don't need to do anything more than allow Him to die. In other words, they believe that everybody is already saved when they are born because Jesus died for everyone.
      3. You must prove their responsibility to accept Christ's payment or to reject it.
      4. Use John 1:12. _____

      _____

      _____

   c. Also use Romans 6:23. The last part of this verse teaches that salvation is a gift. Since it is a gift it must simply be received. A gift isn't really a gift until it has been willingly received. A gift cannot be forced upon its recipient; it must be taken willingly and without attachments.

4. The fourth step is to show how a decision to trust Christ is made.
   a. Romans 10:9-10 _____

   _____

   _____

   b. Notice the Bible says when we *"confess with our mouth (pray) and believe with our heart"* we SHALL BE saved. That leaves no room for doubt if you take God at His word.

5. Calling upon Christ by faith brings salvation.
   a. Romans 10:13 _____

   _____

   _____

    b.   The word *"whosoever"* tells us that anyone and everyone can be saved if they will simply trust Christ by faith to do this work in their lives.

    c.   There is no such thing as someone who is too great a sinner to be forgiven and saved. Hebrews 7:25 _____

_____

_____

6.   Draw in the net. In "fishing for men," we mustn't just give out the wonderful message of salvation and leave without giving the one to whom we have been witnessing an opportunity to trust Christ and be saved.

    a.   Ask the person if he would be willing to bow his head and pray a simple prayer of faith asking the Lord Jesus to forgive his sin and give him His gift of eternal life as He promised.

    b.   This prayer doesn't have to be complicated. Remember the story of the publican who came into God's house and simply prayed, *"God be merciful to me a sinner."* Jesus said that man went home with his sins forgiven and justified.

    c.   If the person to whom you have been witnessing seems to hesitate at this point, ask him if you may lead in a simple sinner's prayer and ask him to pray it with you as you lead.

7.   Teach the truth of assurance to everyone you lead to Christ.

    a.   When one has trusted Christ, it will not be long before the devil comes with his unholy desire to rob the new Christian of his joy which comes from the assurance of his salvation.

    b.   Point out that the Bible teaches (in Romans 8:38-39) there is nothing that can separate the Christian from salvation once he receives this great gift from God.

8.   Remember to do your duty after you have led someone to the Lord.

    a.   Don't forsake those who are babes in Christ.

    b.   It is our duty to follow-up with them, to bring them to church if at all possible, and to help them get rooted and grounded in their new-found faith.

God will bless you as you use these methods to carry this wonderful message to others, and will use you to bring others into the kingdom of His dear Son.

SUMMARY: The only eternal business in which we can all engage is the business of witnessing to the lost and pointing people to Christ so that they might be saved. We who have been saved have been left in this world with a mission. That mission is to bring glory to God and to win others to Christ.

The reasons are many which prove the urgency of our mission. The lost are dying by the thousands every day (Psalm 9:17). God has commanded us to win the lost (Luke 14:23). We are debtors to others; we must tell them of the Gospel (Romans 1:14). Lives can be changed in a wonderful way if they are won to Christ (II Corinthians 5:17).

There comes a time to stop *"talking"* and start *"walking."* That means, of course, there is a time for action. We need to pray, rely upon the Holy Spirit, equip ourselves by memorizing Scripture, and then go out and witness to others. God will help each of us to engage ourselves more in this greatest of all businesses...this business that brings blessings!

REFLECTIONS: Answer the following questions individually or in class. Give careful attention to your answers. This exercise is what the Bible refers to as *meditation.* Think on these things...

1. Who is responsible to win the lost?

_____

_____

2. The Bible tells us to *"go out quickly into the highways and hedges and compel them to come in."* Why is it so urgent to go out quickly?

_____

_____

3. What is promised in Psalm 126:6 to those who will go out with compassion and engage in "bearing the precious seed?"

_____

_____

4. Who is the man in the Bible who won his own brother to Christ? What steps did he use in reaching his goal?

_____

_____

5. What have you learned from the story of Andrew?

_____

_____

6. Why is it important to memorize the "plan of salvation" from Scripture?

_____

_____

7. What lesson do we learn from the example of the Apostle Paul in the matter of witnessing?

_____

—————————————————————————————————
—————————————————————————————————

8. What lessons did you learn from the example of Phillip as you studied this lesson?

—————————————————————————————————
—————————————————————————————————

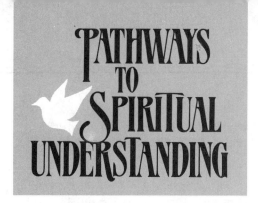

LESSON 15

Sin and Its Effects

MAIN SCRIPTURES:
GENESIS 3:1-19; ROMANS 5:8-12;
EZEKIEL 18:29-32; HEBREWS 11:23-26;
LUKE 22:31; JAMES 1:13-15

LESSON AIM: To learn from Scripture where sin originated and why it is still in the world today. To understand the effects and the consequences of sin upon our lives. To learn how to deal with sin quickly and Scripturally before it works in our lives to do additional damage.

SUGGESTED MEMORY VERSES: Romans 5:12; Psalm 32:1; Galatians 6:7-8; Numbers 32:23; I John 1:9

OVERVIEW:

   I. THE ORIGIN OF SIN

  II. YOU CAN'T HIDE YOUR SIN FOREVER

 III. SIN IS A THIEF

 IV. WHAT CAN WE DO WITH SIN?

INTRODUCTION: "What is the worse thing in the world today?" If someone were to conduct a poll and ask only that question, what kind of answers do you think he would receive? We can guess that some would say cancer is the worse thing in the world today. Others may mention the AIDS crisis that has been unleashed. Still others may reply that war is the worse thing loose in the world today.

Few people stop to think about the real issue behind everything just metnioned. Behind all sickness, famine, war, crime, broken homes and everything else that brings suffering and sorrow is one awful thing—sin.

Sin has made our world a world of suffering, crying, chaos and hatred. It has broken homes, friendships and fellowships for thousands of years. It's something we face and deal with every day of our lives. Yet few people really understand where sin comes from and the effects it has upon all our lives. Even fewer people understand what can be done with sin to minimize its grip upon each of us.

Sin has a great "binding" ability. It has the power to take ahold in lives and, once it has established a grip, is often very difficult to break.

We who know and believe the Bible know that *"where sin abounded, grace did much more abound."* We know that Christ is able to save even the vilest of sinners. What many Christians don't understand is that sin continues to battle us even after we have been saved. We must never give up our defenses in the area of watching for the devil's attack and standing against the sin *"which doth so easily beset us."*

The joyful Christian is the one who has learned to watch out for the danger of sin and to deal with sin quickly before it has an opportunity to make its attachment.

(Where lines are provided after a Scripture reference, look up the verse and write a one sentence summary of what this Scripture is saying to you.)

I.   THE ORIGIN OF SIN

Sin is here; it's a fact. But where did sin begin? To answer that we need to understand and believe the Bible's account in the Book of Genesis.

A.   The *creation* of man

1.   We know that Sin is unique to man, so we must determine where man came from.

   a.   Your belief about the origin of man upon the earth will determine your belief about such things as God, sin, death, morality, Heaven and Hell.

   b.   A proper, Biblical conviction about where man came from is important and vital to your faith!

   c.   Don't let science scare you away from a Biblical stand on creation. Scientists cannot prove even one theory of the origin of man. That's why every one of their ideas is still referred to as a theory. (A theory is an unproven belief. All scientific ideas that go against the Genesis account are only theories.)

2.   There are basically only two scientific theories concerning the origin of man.

   a.   One is called "spontaneous generation." It means that life came from life-less things created through some unknown explosion of matter, which is sometimes called "abiogenesis' or the "big bang theory."

   b.   The second theory is the "theory of natural development," or the "theory of evolution."

      1.   This idea states, basically, that man began millions of years ago as a very basic one-celled creature. (It doesn't offer much of an explanation as to the origin of the one-celled creatures or the world in which they lived.) These one-celled creatures developed over the course of millions of years into modern man.

      2.   The problems with this theory are vast. Too many questions are unanswered. There are gaps between fish, fowl and animal tissue that cannot be explained. There is a division between the species that cannot be explained. No one can explain why, since man has recorded his history, no one ever recorded one event of evolution.

      3.   There is no evidence of anything evolving into a higher form. It is as though evolution ground to a halt.

      4.   If evolution were the basis of life on this planet, it would then, of necessity, be a continuing process.

      5.   These are just a few of the problems

connected with this theory.

6.   It takes greater faith to believe this account than to believe what the Bible records in the Book of Genesis.

3.   The only logical idea about man's origin on the planet earth is found in the Bible.

a.   Genesis 2:7 _____

_____

_____

b.   This account of man's creation gives a basis for understanding what sin is and how it began.

B.   The *condition* of man as God originally created him.

1.   The Bible not only tells us how man was created, but also tells his original condition at creation.

a.   Genesis 1:26-27 teaches that man was created in the *"image of God."*

b.   Man was created in the fashion of God, according to the likeness of God.

2.   Man was created *material* and *immaterial.*

a.   As a material being, man was given a body.

b.   This body was created perfect in its original condition.

c.   As an immaterial being, man was given an immortal soul and spirit.

d.   Genesis 2:7 _____

_____

_____

This is something God didn't give any other part of His creation.

3.   For a while, man lived in this state of perfection as God had originally created him. But something happended to change that.

a.   God created man with a *free will* as evidenced by the choice God gave man in Genesis 2:16-17.

b.   This free will is what eventually opened the door for sin to enter the world.

C.   The *catastrophe* of sin.

1.   In Genesis 3:1-7 we learn what sin is and where sin came from.

a.   Sin is a catastrophe.

b.   Man brought sin into his world by his own choice.

2.   Six downward steps can be seen in the story of how sin entered the world.

a.   In Genesis 3:1, we find that Eve listened to the devil. The very first step to preventing sin is to avoid listening to the devil's enticements.

b.   In Genesis 3:2, Eve lingered too long in the

place of temptation and even carried on a conversation with Satan.

   c.   In Genesis 3:4-5, she allowed the devil to twist and pervert God's word, and she listened as he blatantly denied the honesty of God.

   d.   In Genesis 3:6, Eve fell into the trap of allowing what she saw with lustful eyes to convince her of the devil's lies.

   e.   In the last half of Genesis 3:6, she crossed the line of temptation and actually disobeyed God.

   f.   In Genesis 3:6-7 she included Adam in her sin and they both tried to hide what they had done from God. This is where sin began!

   g.   Proverbs 28:13 _____

       _____

       _____

3.   But what is sin?

   a.   Many people don't understand what sin is. When asked to describe sin, they will usually name a list of sins (such things as murder, envy, lust, adultry, or stealing).

   b.   A good definition for sin is, "an act of willful rebellion against God."

   c.   Sin is a deliberate decision to do, think, speak or act one's own way without regard to God and His Word.

   d.   Sin is not only doing "wrong," sin is also a refusal to do "right." James 4:17 _____

       _____

       _____

D.   The *consequences* of sin.

1.   When Adam and Eve sinned, their sin had immediate consequences upon them and upon the world in which they lived.

   a.   To Eve came sorrow, suffering and subjection. (Genesis 3:16)

   b.   To Adam came sadness, separation and sweat. (Genesis 3:17-19)

2.   Sin is passed through all generations to all generations.

   a.   Romans 5:12 _____

       _____

       _____

   b.   Sin is bound up in the human heart. Jeremiah 17:9 _____

       _____

       _____

3.   Sin had universal consequences to mankind.

    a. Sin brought sickness, pain, aging, suffering and ultimately death.

    b. Sin is the scourge of society.

    c. Sin separates man from God. As it did Adam and Eve, so it still does today. (Isaiah 59:1-2)

E. God has a "cure" for sin.

  1. When man could do no more than hide from God, God came looking for him. What a wonderful testimony to the nature and character of God!

    a. God provided a covering for the shame of Adam and Eve.

    b. Genesis 3:21 _____

    _____

    _____

  2. The cure for sin is God's saving grace, provided through the sacrifice of His Son Jesus Christ.

    a. Titus 3:5 _____

    _____

    _____

    b. Our own good works cannot bring us to God. It takes the mercy of God to span the separation of sin and bring us back into fellowship with God.

II. YOU CAN'T HIDE YOUR SIN FOREVER

Numbers 32:23 teaches sin's ability "to find you out." Most people today are still trying to do what Adam and Eve did with their sin. They are trying to keep it all hidden away. According to God's Word, this is an impossible endeavor. Sin is "Sherlock Holmes," the detective who often works slowly, but in the end always finds his suspect!

Many people live under the false assumption that unless someone reveals their sin to others, no one will ever know; but sin shows up in other ways. In fact, the Bible says that sin shows itself in many, varied ways.

A. Sin may reveal itself in your *conscience.*

  1. Sin has the ability to rob you of peace in your heart, and may even rob you of a sound mind.

    a. Proverb 28:1 _____

    _____

    _____

    b. The wicked flee because of a troubled, haunted conscience.

  2. Sin will rob you of a good night's sleep.

    a. You'll find this truth illustrated in the story of King Darius who couldn't sleep after having Daniel cast into a den of lions (Refer to Daniel 6:16-24.)

    b. Evidently King David lost his peace and had a

troubled conscience because of his sin.
Psalm 51:3 _____

_____

_____

c.   You may sin during the day, but you can count on a troubled conscience when night comes!

B.   Sin will reveal itself in your character.

   1.   If you persist in sinning, it will soon become engrained in your character.

      a.   It's impossible to continue sinning and not have that sin affect your behavior.

      b.   Often when you least expect it to happen, you will slip in the presence of others and you'll be found out.

      c.   A Christian man once began recounting a certain story from His past life. Before he knew it, he became so engrossed in his story that he slipped and used some very profane language. Needless to say, he was embarrassed by what had slipped out of his mouth. The problem was, his sin of profanity had revealed itself.

   2.   It's very difficult to allow sin to take hold in your life for a long period of time and keep it hidden.

      a.   James 1:8 _____

_____

_____

      b.   Judas is an example of a "double-minded" man.

      c.   He tried to cover his sinful character by running with the right crowd until one day his wicked, greedy, deceitful heart exposed him.

      d.   Sin will expose your character when you least expect it to happen.

C.   Sin has a way of revealing itself in your body.

   1.   This Bible principle is taught in Galatians 6:7-8. ____

_____

_____

      a.   According to the Bible, when you "sow to the flesh" you will reap the corruption of the flesh.

      b.   That means when we sin, we will reap the effects of the sin in our body.

   2.   This is very evident in society today.

      a.   We know that alcoholism leads to a weakened heart and liver.

      b.   Smoking leads to respiratory ailments.

      c.   Drug users risk a host of physical problems.

      d.   With the threat of AIDS, an immoral lifestyle is a great physical risk (not to mention the spiritual risk that sin brings).

3. This principle is also illustrated in the life of King David. Almost everyone who has spent any time at all in Bible study knows the story of David's sin. But few people know that his sin affected his flesh.
    a. Read Psalm 38:3-10. You will see from this Psalm that David suffered not only spiritually, but also physically.
    b. Notice Psalm 38:17-18. _____

        _____

        _____

        David knew that he needed to repent and to be sorry for his sin. Physical suffering and weakness only served to remind him of his great need to repent.
    c. His prayer for forgiveness is in Psalm 51.

4. This principle is also taught in I Corinthians 3:16-17.
    a. In this passage Paul warns that defiling the temple of God (which is the body) will lead to its destruction.
    b. We again learn that sin is hard on the body and will shorten one's life (Proverbs 13:15). ___

        _____

    c. Read the wonderful promise of Proverbs 23:2-3 and write the teaching of this passage of Scripture. _____

        _____

        _____

    d. Anyone who has ever spent any time dealing with others in the area of counseling can testify that the results of persistent sin will show up bodily.
    e. Likewise, walking in God's Word will help one avoid some of the sin that others become so entangled in.
    f. Avoiding sin will lead to lengthened days, as we are taught in Proverbs 3.

D. Sin will often reveal itself in the lives of your children.

    1. This principle is not often mentioned, but none the less very true.
        a. That does not necessarily mean that God will make children pay or be accountable for the sin of their parents.
        b. But, sin is often passed on to our children as they observe our behavior.

    2. This Bible principle is also illustrated in the life of King David.
        a. II Samuel 11 relates the account of David taking another man's wife, then attempting to hide his sin by having the husband killed in battle.

    b.   Read the results of David's sin in II Samuel 12:10-15. David's sin resulted in the death of his infant son.

    c.   If you continue reading II Samuel 13, you will read the account of Amnon's sin against his half-sister Tamar. This was the same type of sin committed by his father, David. Amnon had learned this type of reaction and relationship from David.

    d.   The lesson is very easy to see. Children don't always do as they are told. They most often grow up to follow in the steps of those who have influenced them. We who are parents (or who will be) need to remember this principle and let it guide our behavior. David's sin continued to "find him" in the lives of those who had grown up in his own home.

E.   Even if your sin is never revealed while you live on the earth, it will most certainly be revealed on the day of judgment.

    1.   Hebrews 9:27 _____

    _____

    _____

        a.   This day of judgment is a Divine appointment that no one will break.

        b.   Every man, woman and child will someday stand before the Creator of the universe to give account.

    2.   Don't miss the teaching of I Timothy 5:24. _____

    _____

    _____

        a.   Some sins are revealed before we die.

        b.   Others may follow us beyond the grave, but we will give account at that time!

    3.   There is nothing done that God will miss.

        a.   Ecclesiastes 12:14 _____

    _____

    God doesn't miss the good that we do or the bad. (This is not a judgment to determine whether we will go to Heaven or to Hell. That is decided before we die.) This judgment is a day of accounting—the day we must give account of our lives before God.

        b.   Read Psalm 44:21 and Psalm 90:8.

        c.   Basically, for the saved this day of judgment is to determine rewards or loss of rewards.

        d.   For the unsaved, a horrible day of judgment is described in Revelation 20:11-15. This judgment upon the earthly deeds of the

unsaved will determine degrees of eternal
punishment.
4.   You cannot hide your sin forever.
    a.   Sin has multiple ways of finding you.
    b.   Rather than hiding our sin, we must learn how
         to deal with it in a Biblical manner.

III. SIN IS A THIEF

Moses was a very wise man. In Hebrews 11:23-26 we learn
that he chose *"rather to suffer affliction with the people of
God, than to enjoy the pleasures of sin for a season."* If you
listened to the world, you would reach the conclusion that
sin brings only enjoyment and excitement; but there is a lot
about sin that the world just doesn't tell you.

There *is* pleasure in sin. If there were no pleasure in sin
we wouldn't have a problem with it. The pleasure is the bait
the devil uses to enslave people to a life of sin. Moses knew
there was an inescapable law of recompense connected with
sin. He chose to take his stand on God's side rather than to
enjoy the short-lived pleasures of sin.

Sin is a thief. It robs your life of many good things. We will
consider a few of these to encourage you to arrive at the
same conclusion that Moses did several thousand years ago.

A.   Sin robs you of a peaceful mind.

   1.   Remember David's prayer of Psalm 51:3 where he
        said, *"My sin is ever before me."*
        David couldn't forget his sin. No doubt it
        occupied every waking thought and robbed him of
        sleep at night.

   2.   Sin will burn in your mind until it robs you of
        peace.

B.   Sin not only robs you of a peaceful mind, but also steals
     your happiness.

   1.   The devil wants us to believe that happiness can
        only be found in the glitter of the world or in the
        accumulation of material goods.
        This is a lie.
        True happiness, joy and contentment come only
        to those who enjoy a close walk with the Lord.

   2.   Sin always ends in broken hearts and sorrow.
       a.   Even the prodigal son's story proves that sin
            pays off in rags, not riches.
       b.   There is pleasure in sin, but it's short-lived.
            Even then, it isn't worth the price it demands.
            Proverbs 10:27 _____

            _____

            _____

C.   Sin steals the testimony of the Christian.

   1.   The testimony and influence of a Christian is a
        precious thing. A testimony that has taken many

years to build can be broken and destroyed in a matter of moments by sin!

2. Again, an illustration from the life of King David serves best. (II Samuel 11)

   a. David sent the husband of Bathsheba (his name was Uriah) back to the battle, carrying his own death warrant in the form of a letter to David's general, Joab. The letter instructed Joab to send Uriah to the front lines and then allow the others to retreat, leaving him alone. Joab knew that David's intention was to kill Uriah, but Joab's obligation was to fully obey the orders of the King. When the deed was done, Joab sent a message of contempt back to David.

   b. David lost his testimony that day in the eyes of one of his most trusted generals.

   c. II Samuel 12, tells us God sent a prophet named Nathan to David with the story of a man who stole another man's lamb. The purpose of this story was to reveal David's sin of taking Uriah's wife for himself. When the story was told, all the palace knew what their King had done.

3. How awful it is to lose years of good testimony for a few moments of the pleasures of sin.

   When you are tempted by some sin, remember it is a thief and will rob you of that which has taken you years to build. (That, of course, is your testimony and influence.)

D. Sin will steal your good home and marriage.

1. Sin is the number one home-wrecker at work in our society.

   a. The Bible teaches that *"no man lives unto himself and no man dies unto himself."*

   b. What we do has an effect upon others. Often, the effect is felt by those we love the most.

2. The damage that sin can do to the Christian home and marriage is seen in the story of Lot.

   a. Lot was a good man and was raised in a good home.

   b. In fact, he was the nephew to Abraham. (Genesis 11:31) But Lot lost his family to sin.

3. Lot's sin began as materialism.

   a. Genesis 13:10-11 describes the selfish choice Lot made by taking for himself the best of the land.

   b. At first, Lot didn't move into Sodom; he simply moved in that direction.

   c. Perhaps he thought he could provide a better living for his wife and children if he moved into the *"well watered plains of Sodom."*

     d.   This is a dangerous mistake that many Christians make today.

     e.   Believing that it is more important to provide materially for one's family over and above providing that which may be the best spiritually is not a good assumption.

4.   Lot's sin grew to the point that he moved his family into the city of Sodom even though it had a reputation for wickedness. (Genesis 13:13).

     a.   In fact, Lot soon became one of the members of the city government. (Read Genesis 19:1.)

     b.   When the Bible tells us that Lot *"sat in the gate of Sodom,"* it is telling us that he was part of the decision-making body of Sodom. (He became a member of the city council.)

5.   If you read the rest of Lot's story in Genesis 19 you will see how he lost his family to sin.

     a.   When God led Lot's family out of Sodom, his own wife turned back because her heart was still in that wicked city. When she disobeyed God, she died.

     b.   Later, Lot's own daughters caused him to become drunk and commit incest.

     c.   Where did they learn this kind of behavior? The answer of course is, "In Sodom."

     d.   Lot's sin led to the complete destruction of his family.

     e.   Sin is still in the business of destroying families today.

IV. WHAT CAN WE DO WITH SIN?

This last portion of the lesson deals with the sin of the believers.

A.   The believer must recognize temptation as that which leads to sin.

    1.   All sin begins as temptation.

       a.   And all temptation to sin comes from the devil alone!

       b.   God doesn't tempt His own children to sin.

       c.   Read James 1:13-16. Write James 1:14. _____

_____

_____

    2.   If we are to avoid sin, we must first learn to deal with temptation.

       a.   We do that by resisting the devil the moment he tempts us. James 4:7 _____

_____

_____

       b.   Learn to avoid any person or place that might tempt you to sin.

       c.   If you can deal with temptation, you will save

yourself from a lot of the sorrow of sin.

B.   God wants to forgive you after you have crossed over temptation into sin.

   1.   God does not want His children to sin, but when they do He doesn't want them to have to carry the burden of sin and be discouraged by it. Therefore, He teaches us in the Bible what to do with sin.
      a.   I John 1:9 is the "bath tub" for the Christian life! Write this verse and commit it to memory.

      _____

      _____

   2.   What must we do, according to I John 1:9?
      a.   We must confess our sin. This means more than just telling God that we have sinned.
      b.   To confess our sin actually means to agree with God.
      c.   We must see our sin as God sees it. We must agree with Him that what we have done is sin, and sin is that which sent His Son Jesus to die on the cross.
      d.   We must learn to see our sin as dirty and repulsive as God sees it! Anything short of arriving at this conclusion is not confession of sin.

   3.   What is God's promise in I John 1:9?
      a.   He promised to forgive our sin. We can rejoice in the fact that God will erase the memory of our sin from His mind and will use it against us no more! Isaiah 43:25 _____

      _____

      _____

      b.   He promised to cleanse us. (This is a promise about making us clean once again.) After God forgives, we can feel clean on the inside, for He has cleansed us from the unrighteousness that stained our lives. What a wonderful God we have who stands ready to forgive us and to cleanse us from any and all sin if we will confess it to Him.
      c.   Once we have confessed our sin to God, we must trust that He has done His part and has forgiven us. If we don't learn to believe this by our faith in His Word, we are destined to live a miserable life of guilt and burden.
      d.   When God forgives, He forgets!

SUMMARY: I John 2:1 tells us it is God's desire that we not sin. This means God is most pleased when we learn to resist the devil, flee from temptation and avoid the sin which most certainly will ruin our lives and our testimony as a Christian. I John 2:2 tells us that when we sin we have an advocate with the Father. This advocate is none other than Jesus Christ.

According to I John 1:7 it is the precious blood of Christ that *"cleanseth us from all sin."* The word "cleanseth," in the Greek, is a verb in the continuing tense. In other words, the blood of Christ continues to cleanse us. It is the remedy for our sin. When we sin, we have a loving Savior who is waiting to forgive us and to cleanse us so that we may not continually bear the burden and guilt that sin carries with it.

Don't let sin "spend the night" in your life. You must learn to deal with it swiftly. Don't allow any sin to linger in your life. Use I John 1:9 every day to keep it from getting a foothold and bringing with it the destruction that always follows. Sin, if ignored, always grows until it steals the joy from the life of a Christian. Don't let sin become a thief in your life.

REFLECTIONS: Answer the following questions individually or in class. Give careful attention to your answers. This exercise is what the Bible refers to as *meditation.* Think on these things....

1. List one or two things which present problems to those who hold to the theory of evolution.

   _____

   _____

2. In what condition did God originally create man?

   _____

   _____

3. What is a good definition of sin?

   _____

   _____

4. What was the first sin to surface in the world? What resulted after it happened?

   _____

   _____

5. Name at least three ways sin can surface in someone's life.

   _____

   _____

6. Name the Bible character other than King David whose sin showed up in his or her children.

   _____

   _____

7. What is the bait that the devil uses to attract us?

   _____

   _____

8. Sin is a thief. In what ways does it rob us?

   _____

_____

_____

9. How did Lot's path to the backslidden life begin?

_____

_____

10. What one verse teaches Christians what to do with sin after they have already been saved?

_____

_____

11. How does all sin begin? What must we do to learn to avoid sin?

_____

_____

12. List some characteristics of God's forgiveness.

_____

_____

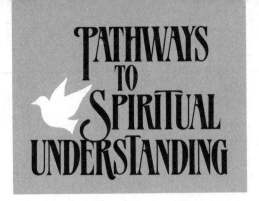

LESSON 16

The Holy Spirit and His Work

MAIN SCRIPTURES:
JOHN 14:16-26; JOHN 16:7-15;
EPHESIANS 2:19-22; ROMANS 8:5-15

LESSON AIM: To lead to the understanding that the third member of the Trinity is God as is the Father and the Son. To lead to a Biblical understanding of the purpose of the Holy Spirit in our lives in the world. To bring us to the conviction that we should yield ourselves to the control of the Holy Spirit.

SUGGESTED MEMORY VERSES:
Luke 11:13; John 14:26; Romans 8:16; I Corinthians 6:19; Ephesians 5:18

OVERVIEW:

   I. THE HOLY SPIRIT, OUR FRIEND WITHIN

  II. UNDERSTANDING THE PERSON AND THE WORK OF THE HOLY SPIRIT

 III. GIVING UP TO THE HOLY SPIRIT

INTRODUCTION: Teachings on the doctrine of the Holy Spirit, like a giant pendulum, swing from one extreme to the other. It is one of the most misunderstood and misused doctrines in the Bible. Yet unless one is aware of the presence of the Holy Spirit living within, and gives attention to His power there can be no victorious Christian living.

Scripture likens the Holy Spirit to the wind. You cannot see the wind, but you can see what the wind is able to do. You cannot see the wind, but you can see the power of the wind at work. You cannot see the wind, but you can harness its power and put it to work for your own help and accomplishment. You cannot see the wind, but you can feel it as it moves.

The Spirit of God is most certainly like the wind in many ways. He cannot be seen, but His power can become a great help as we endeavor to live the Christian life and serve the Lord our God. He cannot be seen, but His presence and influence most certainly can be felt within the heart and life of any Christian who is yielded to Him.

Jesus said, *"And I will pray the Father, and he shall give you another Comforter, that he may abide with you forever."* This comforter, or friend, that Jesus promised to send is the Holy Spirit. How grieved He must be when so very many Christians live as though they don't know Him. We need to learn more about His presence and His work in our lives today. We have the Divine God living within each of us in the person of the Holy Spirit.

(Where lines are provided after Scripture reference, look up the verse and write a one sentence summary of what this Scripture is saying to you.)

I.   THE HOLY SPIRIT, OUR FRIEND WITHIN

A.   The personality of the Holy Spirit

1.   The Holy Spirit is a living personality.

a.   Don't make the mistake of assuming that the Holy Spirit is some type of non-personal member of the Godhead.

b.   The Holy Spirit is a person with all the general characteristics of personality.

c.   Note, in John 14:16-26, how many times Jesus uses personal pronouns such as "he" and "him" when He refers to the Holy Spirit.

d.   Jesus would not use these terms to refer to the Holy Spirit unless the Holy Spirit was to be considered a living personality.

2.   The Bible mentions many ways the Holy Spirit can be treated as a person.

a.   He can be lied to. Acts 5:3 _____

_____

_____

b.   The Spirit can be tempted. Acts 5:9 _____

_____

_____

c.   He can be resisted. Acts 7:51 _____

_____

_____

d.   He has feelings, as we do, and He can be grieved. Ephesians 4:30 _____

_____

_____

e.   He has the ability to reason, to think, to choose and to speak. These are all characteristics of personality. (Acts 13:1-2)

3.   The Holy Spirit is not a thing. Nor is He to be considered as some force at work in the world. He is a living member of the Trinity with feelings and personality.

a.   When speaking to the Holy Spirit or about the Holy Spirit, we ought to use words like "he" and "him" rather than the word "it."

B.   The Holy Spirit's Deity is taught in the Bible.

1.   He is God; the Bible calls Him God!

a.   In the story of the sin of Ananias and his wife Sapphira recorded in Acts 5, the Holy Spirit is referred to as *"God"* in verse 4.

b.   I Corinthians 3:16 teaches that the body of every saved person is the temple (or the dwelling place) of God. The God that indwells is the Holy Spirit. Write I Corinthians 3:16. ___

———————————————————————

———————————————————————

2. In other passages in the Bible, the Holy Spirit is
    identified as not only being "with" God, but as
    being God, Himself.
    a. He is present in the creation of man. Genesis
        1:26 ——————————————————————

        ———————————————————————

        ———————————————————————

        Notice the plural terms that are used in this
        verse. *"Let us make man in our image...."*
        This is evidence of each member of the Trinity
        being present at creation.
    b. At the judgment of Babel, the Holy Spirit is
        present. (Genesis 11:5-8)
    c. The Holy Spirit was present at the baptism of
        the Lord Jesus. (Luke 3:21-22)
    d. The Holy Spirit is included in the great
        commission. Matthew 28:19 ——————————

        ———————————————————————

        ———————————————————————

3. The Holy Spirit has all the divine attributes of God.
    a. He is eternal. Hebrews 9:14 ——————————

        ———————————————————————

        ———————————————————————

    b. The Holy Spirit is omnipresent. Psalm 139:7 ——

        ———————————————————————

        ———————————————————————

    c. The Holy Spirit is all powerful. Luke 1:35 ——

        ———————————————————————

        ———————————————————————

    d. He possesses all the attributes of God, further
        assuring us that He is Divine.

II. UNDERSTANDING THE PERSON AND THE WORK OF THE HOLY SPIRIT

The work and ministry of the Holy Spirit hasn't changed
through the years. His primary mission in the world is to
convict the unsaved of their sins and their need for the
Savior, and to indwell those who are saved. Read Ephesians
2:19-22; Ephesians 4:4-6 and Ephesians 5:18.

A. The meaning of the Holy Spirit

1. We have already established the fact that the Holy
    Spirit is a living member of the Godhead.
    a. He is not just an influence, a force or a make-
        believe character. The Holy Spirit is a person.

      b.   What else do we need to know about the person of the Holy Spirit?

2.   He is God's direct presence upon the earth.

      a.   When we say, "God is with me," it is the Holy Spirit to whom we are referring.

      b.   When we say, "God is working in my life," it is the Holy Spirit that is working in our lives.

      c.   When we say, "The Lord is leading me, speaking to me, or convicting me," it is the Holy Spirit that leads us, speaks to us and convicts us.

      d.   The Holy Spirit is God at work in our lives.

3.   The Holy Spirit indwells every person who has been born again.

      a.   One cannot be saved apart from being indwelt by the Holy Spirit! Romans 8:9 _____

            _____

      b.   The indwelling Spirit of God bears witness with our own spirit to let us know we have been saved. Romans 8:16 _____

            _____

      c.   According to Ephesians 4:6, God is in all who have been saved. The God within is the Holy Spirit.

4.   The Holy Spirit longs to control the life of every Christian.

      a.   Romans 6:19 says, *"...even so now yield your members servants to righteousness unto holiness."* We need to learn to yield our bodies to the leadership and control of the Holy Spirit.

      b.   The Holy Spirit will not seize control by force, but He longs for us to willingly and lovingly present ourselves to Him. Romans 12:1-2 _____

            _____

      c.   The life of joy, peace, contentment, assurance and fruitfulness begins with yielding control of our lives to the Holy Spirit.

      d.   When the Holy Spirit is in control, you can rest assured that He will lead you in the right direction and choose the best for your life when decisions must be made.

B.   The might of the Holy Spirit

    1.   The Holy Spirit has great power. This power is available to every child of God to help live the life of victory in the world.

    a.   Read Ephesians 1:19 and Ephesians 3:20. What did you learn from these two passages? _____

_____

    b.   Read Colossians 1:10-11 and Colossians 1:29. The word *"working"* found in Colossians 1:29 is a Greek word meaning *"energy."* Paul is saying in this verse, "I labour, striving according to HIS ENERGY which worketh in me mightily."

    c.   We need to learn to serve and labor for the Lord not in our own strength, but in His energy and power.

        1.   This is the power and energy of the Holy Spirit.

        2.   This energy is the power that kept the Apostle Paul serving the Lord in faith and courage until it was time for him to go to Heaven.

        3.   This same power will help each of us today, not only to serve the Lord with effectiveness, but also to live the Christian life.

2.   The Holy Spirit has power over numbers.

    a.   This fact has been proven over and over again in the Bible.

    b.   The entire Egyptian population was against Moses, yet God used Moses to lead His people out of Egypt and out of slavery by His power.

    c.   Elijah knew what it was to stand against great odds. I Kings, chapter 18 has the account of Elijah standing alone against Ahab, Jezebel, and 850 false prophets. The outcome is victory for Elijah, who knew the power of God and wasn't afraid of the numbers that stood against him.

    d.   Gideon had only 300 men to stand against the Midianites; he had also the power of God upon his life. The outcome for Gideon was victory over the numbers that stood against him and against God's people.

    e.   From II Kings chapter 6 we learn how God's power delivered Elisha from the armies of Ben-hadad, king of Syria.

    f.   The power of God, available through the indwelling Spirit, is able to overcome great odds.

3.   The Holy Spirit is able to overcome any and all circumstances that may arise in our lives.

    a.   Any task, no matter how difficult, can be accomplished in the power and energy of the Holy Spirit.

    b.   Samson was able to slay 1,000 Philistines who were the avowed enemies of God and God's people, with nothing more than the jawbone of a donkey. Why? According to Judges 15:14 it was because *"the Spirit of the Lord came mightily upon him...."*

c. We may not be called upon to fight the Philistines with the jawbone of the donkey, but we do face battles in the Christian life that are just as serious. We need to learn to depend upon the power of the Holy Spirit to help us in such circumstances.

4. The Holy Spirit is greater than any obstacle or difficulty.

a. God's power is able to make up that which is lacking in the life of anyone who will serve the Lord. His power is able to overcome any obstacle the devil may throw in our way to keep us from living as we should, and anything he does to keep us from serving the Lord with faithfulness. The examples in the Bible are numerous.

1. Moses had a speech problem; but with God's help and power it didn't hinder him from serving the Lord.

2. Gideon argued with the Lord that he was the "least of all his family." That means he felt unable to do what God called him to do. Yet with God's help and power upon his life, Gideon brought victory to God's people.

3. In Daniel, chapter 3, we find the story of three Hebrew men who were slaves in Babylon. They refused to bow down to an idol built by King Nebuchadnezzar. Because they stayed true to their God, Nebuchadnezzar had them tossed into a furnace of fire. God met them in the firey furnace and delivered them by His great power! When we face the fires of adversity today, God is still able to deliver us!

4. Paul and Silas were falsely accused and locked into a prison in the city of Philippi. They kept their spirits up and their hearts right, even though they had been grossly mistreated (this is difficult for many to do even today). In Acts 16:25-26 we learn how God caused an earthquake to shake the doors off their hinges and free Paul and Silas from their captivity. Once again we see how God is able, by His great power, to overcome any obstacle or difficulty that comes along.

b. This very same God is our God today! His power hasn't diminished over the years. His power and strength have been promised to every Christian who will learn what it is to be yielded to the Holy Spirit. There is no obstacle that cannot be overcome with the power of God.

C. The motive for submitting to the leadership and control of the Holy Spirit.

1. The Holy Spirit is our friend and helper.
    a. We need to understand why it is important to willingly yield our lives to His complete control.
    b. Without the right motives, our actions cannot be right. Many Christians fear surrendering to the Holy Spirit's leading in their lives. The benefits the Holy Spirit brings when He is in control of one's life far outweight any reasons to fear total surrender of our lives to the Lord.

2. We need Him because He is the comforter.
    a. Jesus referred to the Holy Spirit as the comforter in John 14:16.
    b. As our comforter, He will bring peace to our lives when we face difficult times or circumstances. This is His duty!
    c. Job was a man who lived with his heart completely yielded to the Lord. Only the Lord's ability to comfort Job could help him say what he did when news reached him of the loss of his cattle, his camels, his donkeys, his servants and his ten children. (Psychologists today report the death of a child as one of the most traumatic events a parent can experience.) Read the words of Job as recorded in Job 1:20-22 after all his losses.

        _____

        _____

    d. *"In all this Job sinned not, nor charged God foolishly."* Job knew something of God's ability to comfort even in adverse circumstances.
    e. Everyone eventually needs a comforter. The Holy Spirit is a comforter who will never fail.

3. We need Him because He is our teacher.
    a. Read and record what you learn from John 14:26. _____

        _____

    b. The Holy Spirit is the author of the Bible. We are told in II Peter 1:21 that *"holy men of God spake as they were moved by the Holy Ghost."* What better teacher of the Bible could you find than the one who is the very author?
    c. When you open your Bible to read and to study, don't fail to begin with a brief prayer

asking the Holy Spirit to open your heart to understand the Word of God.

d.   The Holy Spirit longs to help God's people as they study the Bible. He is our teacher. What does John 14:26 teach you? _____

_____

_____

4.   We need Him because He is our guide in life.
a.   The Holy Spirit, being God, knows all the best choices for our lives. He knows the best path for us to walk.
b.   We must learn to include Him in our prayers, and seek His peace when it comes to making decisions. How tragic it is when Christians make all their decisions with the "head" and not with the "heart."
c.   In Acts chapter 16 you'll find that the Apostle Paul intended to go to Asia; but according to verse 6, he was *"forbidden of the Holy Ghost"* and was led to Philippi where he was successful in starting another church. We, too, must learn to listen for the leading of the Holy Spirit.
d.   In Colossians 3:15 we learn a tremendous Bible principle. _____

_____

_____

The principle of this verse teaches us that we are to allow God's peace to make the decisions in life. The word "rule" comes from a Greek word that means "umpire." Now, everyone knows it is the duty of the umpire to rule and to make the decisions. In the sports world, the umpire is the judge. His is the final decision. We need to learn to seek God's peace in all decisions. When we do this, we are learning to allow the Holy Spirit to guide our lives, and we're learning to make decisions that please the Lord.

5.   We need Him because He is the one whose help produces godliness in our lives.
a.   Read Galatians 5:22-23. List what the Bible refers to as *"the fruit of the Spirit."* _____

_____

_____

b.   These characteristics make up godliness. They are the traits the Holy Spirit desires to produce in the life of every saved person.
c.   These qualities cannot be bought, borrowed, or bargained for. They must be produced by

            yielding to the Holy Spirit.

    d.   The Holy Spirit can produce these wonderful products of Christian character in the life of any and every saved person who places his life in the Lord's hands to be shaped and molded. It is the Holy Spirit's power that produces a godly life.

D.   The method of being filled with the power of the Holy Spirit.

    1.   Much misunderstanding exists today about what it means to be *"filled with the Holy Spirit"* and how one can be filled.

        a.   God doesn't give the power of the Holy Spirit just so we may have some wonderful, emotional, uplifting experience. God gives His power in order that we may live the Christian life with a good testimony and use His power in our lives to serve Him effectively.

        b.   God's power is for doing God's work! Just as an automobile needs to have its tank filled in order to serve its owner and do what it was purchased to do, so we need God's power in our lives to do the work that He has given us to do. And just as an automobile needs to be refilled many times over the course of its life, so we too must learn this principle.

        c.   There is only one *baptism* of the Holy Spirit. That takes place when He places us within the family of God at the moment of our conversion. Ephesians 4:4-6 _____

            _____

            _____

        d.   The baptism of the Spirit is an act of the Holy Spirit whereby He places us into the family of God when we are saved. If you search the Scripture you will find no command to seek the baptism of the Spirit. This is the work of the Holy Spirit and not a work that we do. It is that which He does for us. I Corinthians 12:13

            _____

            _____

        e.   We do find a command to be *"filled with the Spirit"* in Ephesians 5:18 _____

            _____

            _____

    2.   We will see what it means to be filled with the Spirit in the remaining portion of this lesson. The "filling" of the Holy Spirit has to do with his control and His power for service. Basically, three things are

necessary to be filled with the Spirit.

a.   There must be a desire to be filled.

1.   This may sound very basic, but the truth is, many Christians don't have much of God's power at work in their lives because they don't want God's power.

2.   In Isaiah 44:3 the Lord said, *"I will pour water upon him that is thirsty, and floods upon the dry ground; I will pour my Spirit upon thy seed, and my blessing upon thine offspring."* You must have a thirst for God's power in your life. This means you must have a desire.

b.   There must be an "emptying of self" in the areas of sin, wrong relationships and improper attitudes.

1.   The Lord cannot fill a heart that is already full of other things. We must first make room for the Lord in our hearts, and we must make a heart for Him that is as clean as we can make it.

2.   Read Galatians 5:17-26 and record some of the lessons or principles you find in this portion of Scripture. _____

_____

_____

3.   The flesh and the Spirit are at odds with one another. God cannot fill a life with His Spirit when that life is already filled with things of the flesh.

3.   We must pray and ask the Lord to fill us with His power and Spirit.

1.   Luke 11:13 _____

_____

_____

2.   Pray and ask the Lord to fill your life with the Spirit's power so that you may live pleasing to Him and serve Him effectively. With these motives and desires, the Lord is well pleased.

III. GIVING UP TO THE HOLY SPIRIT

Read Romans 12:1-2. These verses teach about practical Christianity. It isn't a suit and tie that makes one a Christian, nor going to church, nor even carrying a Bible. It's the Holy Spirit living on the inside that produces a new life, according to II Corinthians 5:17. Being a Christian MUST become more than just something we *are;* it must become what we *do!*

The word Christian means *"Christ-like."* If we are to become more Christ-like, we must do what we are taught in Romans 12:1-2: surrender our lives to the Lord as "living sacrifices." We are commanded by God to be filled with the

Holy Spirit, or to be controlled by the Holy Spirit.

In Ephesians 5:18, we are commanded not to be drunk with wine. When a man is drunk, he is being controlled by the alcohol in his system. It affects the way he thinks, speaks, walks and acts. Likewise, when a man is filled with the Holy Spirit, the Spirit affects the way he thinks, speaks, walks and acts.

On the day of Pentecost, when the disciples were filled with the power of the Holy Spirit, they were falsely accused of being drunk (Acts 2:15). The residents of Jerusalem saw a change in these men. They changed from men who were hiding to men filled with joy and boldness. Therefore, observers falsely assumed they were drinking.

The Holy Spirit does produce joy and boldness in the lives of those who are filled with His power. The Holy Spirit longs to do His work in your life. However you must first present your life to Him as outlined in Romans 12:1-2. In essence, you must give up your ways for His ways, and your will for His will. There are five areas of life the Holy Spirit wants to control.

A.   He wants to control our lips.

1.   More damage is done to the work of God by uncontrolled lips than by any other single tool of the devil!

a.   Pastors, evangelists, missionaries and even laymen have been destroyed by the words of people whose tongues were not yielded to the Spirit's complete control.

2.   Wrong words have great destructive ability.

a.   Proverbs 18:8 _____

_____

_____

Some words inflict mortal wounds.

b.   Read what Job asked his friends in Job 19:1-2.

3.   God's Word clearly admonishes us to speak only words that are "Spirit-controlled."

a.   Ephesians 4:29 _____

_____

_____

b.   Any communication that is curt, cutting, cruel, cold, caustic or critical is corrupt!

c.   Matthew 12:36 warns us that someday we will answer to the Lord for our words.

B.   The Spirit wants to control our hearts.

1.   The "heart" refers to the inner spirit each of us possesses.

a.   Many Christians today could be summed up in the word of Matthew 15:8 _____

_____

_____

     b.   Luke 16:15 says, *"for God knoweth your heart."* God has the ability to look beyond the exterior to the inside.

     c.   He knows the attitudes and feelings hidden away inside.

  2.   The Holy Spirit wants us to give Him our hearts so He can help us control our thoughts, desires and attitudes.

     a.   Read Ephesians 3:16-17. Paul's prayer for the Ephesian Christians was that they might be strengthened in the inner man (heart and spirit) by the power of the Holy Spirit.

     b.   The Holy Spirit is able to strengthen our inner man with His power.

     c.   I Corinthians 6:20 commands that we glorify God both in body and in spirit. That means that our attitude and temperaments are to bring God glory, but many Christians don't glorify God by the spirit they display before others.

     d.   Not one attitude, one emoton or even one feeling should be harbored in our hearts that would grieve God's Holy Spirit.

C.   The Holy Spirit wants control of our minds.

  1.   Why should you allow the Spirit to control your mind?

     a.   Proverbs 23:7 teaches that a man's thoughts produce his actions.

     b.   Proper thought will produce proper actions.

     c.   Likewise, improper thoughts will produce improper actions.

  2.   Most sin begins as a thought.

     a.   The devil cannot make anyone sin. He can only plant little thoughts about sinning in our minds.

     b.   If one thinks hateful thoughts, he will be a hateful person; bitter thoughts, a bitter person; proud thoughts, a proud person, discouraging thoughts, a discouraged person.

  3.   If the Holy Spirit can help you control your mind and lead you to think Christ-like thoughts, He'll produce more "Christ-likeness" in your life.

     a.   *"As a man thinketh in his heart, so is he."*

     b.   II Corinthians 10:5 _____

        _____

        _____

        We need to learn to cast down every wicked imagination (or thoughts), and bring into captivity every thought.

     c.   Very simply put, the principle teaches us to control what we think. With the Spirit's help this is possible.

D.   The spirit wants control of our desires.

1.   There is an internal battle for control of desires that goes on in the life of every Christian.

a.   The Spirit battles against the flesh, or the old nature. The flesh battles against the Spirit, or the new nature given to us when we were saved.

b.   I Peter 2:11 tells us we are to *"abstain from fleshly lusts, which war against the soul."*

2.   Uncontrolled desires have put many men in trouble in the past.

a.   David desired another man's wife.

b.   Achan desired the gold and silver of Jericho.

c.   Gehazi desired the wealth of Naaman.

d.   Judas desired the silver of the Pharisees.

e.   It's true! Fleshly lusts war against the soul. We must learn to pray for the Holy Spirit's control over our desires.

E.   The Holy Spirit wants to control our bodies.

1.   The body of the believer is where the Holy Spirit dwells (I Corinthians 6:19). It's only natural that He wants to control His own dwelling.

2.   Many Christians struggle with controlling the flesh when, according to the Bible, it is more a matter of yielding the body to the Lord, seeking His help and power, rather than trying to control the flesh by our own strength alone.

a.   Read Romans 6:11-19. We become servants to whom we yield ourselves—whether to sin or to the Savior.

b.   Read and record Galatians 2:20. _____

_____

_____

c.   Ask God to help you yield yourself to the Spirit's control so you, too, may be able to say, *"The life which I now live in the flesh I live by the faith of the Son of God, who loved me, and gave Himself for me."*

SUMMARY: There is still much confusion over the doctrine of the Holy Spirit. Make sure you get your doctrine and convictions from the Bible, and not from any other source. The Holy Spirit was given to us to help us live as we should and serve the Lord as we ought until either He returns, or we are taken to Heaven by death. The Holy Spirit is our comforter, guide, teacher, helper and friend. We need to learn to willingly give Him our lives in complete and total surrender. Only then will we experience all the help He is able to provide. He doesn't take over any area of our lives by force; He only takes control of those areas yielded to Him. So, many Christians live defeated lives, having been deceived by the devil.

Many have been fooled into believing when they surrender to

the Lord He will call them into full-time Christian service and send them to some remote island to become missionaries. (If the Lord ever did call you to be a missionary you should rejoice at His call upon your life and realize that you will never be happy in any endeavor of life if you aren't in God's will.) For the vast majority of Christians however, God's will doesn't involve full time service; it only involves living the life of a good ambassador for Christ and serving the Lord in some local church ministry with whatever skills or abilities He has given. This kind of life isn't to be feared; it's to be enjoyed!

When you let God make the choices in your life, He will always choose the best for you. Learn all you can about the blessed Holy Spirit. Get a thirst for His power to work in your life, empty your life of any sinful attitudes or actions that have hindered your Christian growth, then pray that God will fill you with the power of the Spirit. There is no life sweeter than the life of a Christian filled with and controlled by God's Holy Spirit.

REFLECTIONS: Answer the following questions individually or in class. Give careful attention to your answers. This exercise is what the Bible refers to as *meditation*. Think on these things....

1. In the Bible, the Holy Spirit is likened to the wind. In what ways is this symbolism true?

   _____

   _____

2. In what ways can the Holy Spirit be treated like any other person?

   _____

   _____

3. List a reason or two that leads us to the conviction that the Holy Spirit is God.

   _____

   _____

4. Who is indwelt by the Spirit? When does this take place?

   _____

   _____

5. Why do you need the power of the Holy Spirit in your life?

   _____

   _____

6. For what purposes did the Lord Jesus send the Holy Spirit to the world after His own ascension? What is His mission?

   _____

   _____

7. What are we to seek when asking the Holy Spirit's help in life's decisions?

   _____

   _____

8. What traits are listed in the Bible as the fruit of the Spirit? What does it mean to say these things are the fruit of the Spirit?

   _____

   _____

9. What are the three basic steps necessary to understand how to be filled with the Spirit?

   _____

   _____

10. What does it mean to be filled with the Spirit as commanded in Ephesians 5:18?

    _____

    _____

11. What areas of life should we allow the Holy Spirit to control?

    _____

    _____

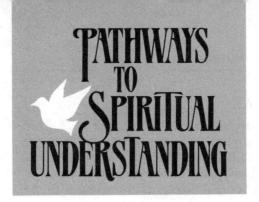

LESSON 17

The Return of Christ and Judgment

MAIN SCRIPTURES:
MATTHEW 24:1-14; I CORINTHIANS 15:51-58; I THESSALONIANS 4:13-18; TITUS 2:11-15;
II TIMOTHY 3:1-5; REVELATION 19:11-16; REVELATION 20:11-15

LESSON AIM: To lead to a Biblical understanding of the return of the Lord Jesus. To understand how His coming to earth is divided into two parts, separated by a period of time called "the tribulation." To understand what the Bible teaches about the judgment of the saved and the unsaved.

SUGGESTED MEMORY VERSES:
John 14:3; Acts 1:11; II Corinthians 5:10; Titus 2:13; Revelation 22:12

OVERVIEW:

    I. JESUS IS COMING AGAIN!

    II. INDICATORS THAT POINT TO THE DAY OF THE LORD'S RETURN.

    III. THE JUDGMENT OF THE SAVED AND THE UNSAVED.

INTRODUCTION: Acts, chapter one, records the story of the ascension of the Lord Jesus into Heaven. As a group of His devoted followers stood looking up into the clouds where Jesus had just vanished an angel made a profound announcement. The angel said, *"Ye men of Galilee, why stand ye gazing up into heaven? This same Jesus, which is taken up from you into heaven, shall so come in like manner as ye have seen him go into heaven."* In Revelation 22:12 we read the words of Jesus as they were given to the Apostle John on the Isle of Patmos, *"Behold, I come quickly; and my reward is with me, to give every man according to his works."*

The most oft-asked questions are questions relating to the coming of the Lord and the judgment that is to come someday upon the earth in the form of seven years of tribulation. Everybody wants to know, "Is Jesus really going to return to the earth? Will He come visibly? When is He going to return? Are there any signs to point to His coming?"

Jesus is going to return to the earth again someday. His appearing will be both visible and bodily. We aren't to fear living in these days. In fact, there has been no better time to be a Christian than the time in which we live. We have many advantages the generations before us didn't have. And, we are living closer to the coming of the Lord than any other generation of Christians that has ever lived.

Titus said the Lord's returning to the earth is to be counted as our "blessed hope." That means something to be longed for and anticipated. We are living in what the Bible calls "the latter days." If any generation should be prepared for the Lord's return, it should be ours.

(Where lines are provided after a Scripture reference, look up the verse and write a one sentence summary of what this Scripture is saying to you.)

I. JESUS IS COMING AGAIN!

The Lord's return to the earth is divided into two parts. The first has been called the rapture of the saints. While the word *"rapture"* isn't found in the Bible, the principle and the truth of the rapture most certainly is. (Read I Thessalonians 4:13-18.) The Book of Revelation also teaches the truth of the rapture.

In Revelation, chapters 1-3, the Apostle John is on the Isle of Patmos where he was exiled because of his preaching and his testimony. He wrote what he saw from his place there on the Isle. In chapter 4, a transition is made. In verse one, John heard a voice that called him up to heaven. This is a "type," or a symbol, of the rapture which is taught in I Thessalonians 4:13-18 and in I Corinthians 15:51-58.

You will notice another wonderful teaching in Revelation 4:2. After he heard the voice that called him to Heaven, he was "immediately" in the throne room of Heaven. Everything mentioned after Revelation 4:1 and 2, and before 19:11, is a prophecy of what will happen in the seven-year period of time referred to as the tribulation. Revelation 19:11-21 refers to the second coming of Christ, when Jesus will actually return to the earth according to the promise of John 14 and Acts 1. Let's look at three simple facts about the Lord's return.

A. His return is a reality.

   1. There are many today who scoff at such a claim.

   2. These scoffers are a fulfillment of Bible prophecy. II Peter 3:3-4 _____

   _____

   _____

   3. Others ask, "Why has the Lord not yet returned?"
       a. The answer is found in II Peter 3:9 _____

       _____

       _____

          1. God is longsuffering and is *"not willing that any should perish."*
          2. God's patience has caused the return of Jesus to be delayed to this late day. God, in His great love and mercy, wants to see people saved and escape eternity in hell.

       b. There will come the day when God's patience with the world draws to an end. Jesus will then return. Only God knows when that will be.

   4. The return of the Lord is literal!
       a. It is "according to the letter," or, just exactly as the Bible declares.
       b. The angels' message in Acts 1:11 states that Jesus will come in the same manner as He went away.
       c. This tells us much about the manner of the Lord's return.

1. He went away bodily, and He shall return bodily.
2. He went away visibly, and He shall return visibly.
3. He went away in the clouds, and He shall return in the clouds.
4. He went away in the presence of Believers only, and at the rapture He shall return for Believers only.

5. Not only is His return literal, but it will also be sudden.
    a. I Corinthians 15:51 says it this way: *"In a moment, in the twinkling of an eye...."*
    b. Matthew 24:27 says about the swiftness of His return, it will be *"as the lightning cometh out of the east, and shineth even unto the west: even so shall also the coming of the Son of man be."*
    c. His return will be a sudden event.

6. His return will be unexpected.
    a. Read I Thessalonians 5:2 and write a brief summary about the Lord's return. _____
        _____
        _____

    b. A thief always comes when his appearance is least expected. Most of the world today isn't looking for Jesus to return. Remember, *"in an hour when ye think not"* is what the Bible has to say about the time of His appearing.

7. His return will be glorious for those who anticipate it and have prepared themselves.
    a. Titus called this day of the Lord's return *"our blessed hope."* That is something to look forward to.
    b. His coming will be a glorious event and ought to be a blessed day of anticipation for those who know Christ as their Savior.

B. The results of His return

1. There is not one person upon the earth who won't be affected by the Lord's return.
    a. Almost immediately, the effects will be seen, heard and felt by all.
    b. From this point on, the lives of every person will be changed forever.

2. The first, immediate effect will be the disappearance of hundreds of thousands, or perhaps even millions of people.
    a. Those who disappear in the rapture will be the living Believers.
    b. Those who know Christ as their Savior and who are living when He returns will suddenly

find their mortal bodies changed into new immortal, spiritual bodies. I Corinthians 15:53

_____

_____

_____

    c.   Then, they will be "caught up" to meet the Lord in the air. I Thessalonians 4:17 _____

           _____

           _____

3.   The graves of those who died as Believers will be opened, and new, glorified bodies will be brought out of the space where once mortal bodies had been laid to rest.

    a.   In fact, this event will happen just before the living Believers are caught up. I Thessalonians 4:16 _____

           _____

    b.   Then, together we go to meet the Lord in the air and, as the Bible says in I Thessalonians 4:17, *"So shall we ever be with the Lord."*

4.   This Scripture and this principle doesn't teach the idea of "soul sleep," which simply means that those who have died are sleeping in the grave and have no conscious existence until the time of Christ's return.

    a.   The Bible teaches that at the moment the physical body dies, the soul and spirit depart for only one of two destinations—heaven or hell.

    b.   Notice what the Bible teaches in II Corinthians 5:8 about the soul and spirit of the Christian at death. _____

           _____

    c.   When a saved person dies physically, his soul and spirit will move immediately into the presence of the Lord! If this weren't so, why would the Apostle Paul have said, *"for me to die is gain"* in Philippians 1:21? Note, too, what he writes in Philippians 1:23. _____

           _____

           _____

    d.   The graves of those who die believing in the Lord Jesus will be opened as a witness and testimony to the truth of the Bible and as evidence that Jesus has returned as promised.

5.   All of this takes place in a moment of time.

    a.   In fact, the Bible says it will all happen in the *"twinkling of an eye."* I Corinthians 15:52.

6.   Think of all the circumstances that will surround the sudden disappearance of millions of living people!

    a.   The air will be filled with the sound of sirens rushing to the scene of many accidents.

    b.   Drivers will disappear from their automobiles and buses.

    c.   Christian pilots will disappear from the cockpits of their airplanes.

    d.   Factories will close as many workers don't report to work.

    e.   Parents will phone the police to report the sudden disappearance of their children.

    f.   Police and fire efforts will be hampered because policemen and firemen who are Christians will be going with the Lord when He returns at the time of rapture.

    g.   There are many, many more circumstances that will surround the return of the Lord. These have been mentioned to show you the worldwide effect this event will have. There isn't a home or a person who won't be touched in some way.

7.   Soon after the rapture takes place, a new world leader will appear on the scene. He will be a man of such charisma and charm that most of the world will embrace him as the leader of the world's governments. He is the anti-Christ.

    a.   He is described in symbolic terms in Revelation 13:1-10. He is the devil in the flesh and will deceive most of the world into giving him worldwide power.

    b.   The anti-Christ will, in his initial days of power, solve the world's problems of war, famine and division. Later, he will declare himself as the Messiah and demand worship and obeisance. Those who refuse to worship and obey him will suffer dire consequences. Read Revelation 13:16-17 for an idea of his power over the people.

    c.   He will have a companion in his desire for world control.

        1.   The Bible calls this second "beast" the false prophet.

        2.   In Revelation 13:11-15 he is described in a peculiar way. Verse 11 says, *"He had two horns like a lamb, and he spake as a dragon."*

        3.   This shows his true character. He portrays himself as a lamb. He pretends to be a great religious leader and, according to Revelation 17:1-7, he will head up a

world religious system.

4. In reality he is a dragon! His vicious
    nature is seen in Revelation 13:15-16. He
    won't tolerate those who refuse to follow
    his demands and he will persecute and
    torment people into obeying him.

8. After the rapture of the Church, the world will
    suffer seven years of God's judgment. This time is
    called the *"tribulation."*
    a. Jesus described it as the most awful time to
        ever fall upon the earth. Matthew 24:21 _____

        _____

    b. He further stated that if the days of the
        tribulation weren't shortened, there would be
        no one left alive on the earth. Matthew 24:22 _

        _____

    c. The description of this time and of the actual
        judgments begin in Revelation chapter 6, and
        continue through Revelation chapter 16. These
        judgments are not symbolic. They are literal
        judgments which God will pour out upon a
        world that has rejected and will continue to
        reject Christ! There are three groups of seven
        judgments.
        1. One group is called the seven *"seals"*.
        2. One is called the seven *"trumpets."*
        3. The last is called the seven *"vials.*
    d. Revelation, chapter 17, shows the collapse of
        the world religious system and the doom of
        the world church.
    e. Revelation chapter 18 says the world
        government of the anti-Christ will fall in
        around him. This collapse will happen
        suddenly, according to Revelation 18:17.

9. Revelation, chapter 19, shows Jesus' return to the
    earth! This is the Second Coming of Christ.
    a. He comes in great power and glory! Revelation
        19:11-16 gives a description of His return.
    b. He returns to conquer and judge the anti-
        Christ and the false prophet. Revelation 19:20 _

        _____

    c. He returns to establish his kingdom upon the
        earth (that will last for 1,000 years). Read
        Revelation 20:1-6. This period of time is the
        blessed time of the kingdom of God upon the
        earth. At the end of this time, Jesus the
        righteous judge, will judge all those who
        rejected Him as Savior.

    d.   This judgment is described in Revelation 20:11-15.

C.   The reaction and response of those who say they believe the Lord will return soon.

    1.   Our beliefs always have certain effects upon our actions. That principle is true in the life of everyone. What we believe affects what we do.

        If we say we believe the Lord will return to earth soon, that belief ought to have a profound effect upon the way we live!

    2.   One who is looking for the Lord to return is different in his *worship.*

        a.   He doesn't have to be begged to attend Church on Sunday. There is no other place he wants to be, just in case the Lord returns on Sunday.

        b.   He doesn't have to be entertained to keep his attention on the sermon. He listens with great interest, for every sermon could be the last sermon before Jesus returns.

        c.   You don't have to plead with him to find a place of service in the church ministries. He finds a place to serve and gives his best.

        d.   He doesn't have to be coaxed into giving. He delights in the privilege of giving to advance the cause of Christ's work.

    3.   One who is looking for the Lord to return is different in his *work.*

        a.   He realizes the brevity of time and gives his best and most faithful service to every work.

        b.   His motivation comes from a love for the Lord and a desire to please Him rather than a desire to be seen of men.

        c.   He works with excitement and enthusiasm, knowing that every day could be the day the Lord returns.

    4.   One who is looking for the Lord to return is different in his *witness.*

        a.   He is a Christian with compassion in his heart for those who are lost.

        b.   He works without complaint so that others may hear the Gospel.

        c.   He gives to missions so that others may have the opportunity to be saved before Christ returns.

        d.   Who would you witness to if you knew, without doubt, that Jesus would return before the end of the week? Remember, Jesus said, *"Behold, I come quickly."*

    5.   One who is looking for the Lord to return is different in his *walk.*

        a.   His conduct before others each day is different

from those who don't really believe that Jesus could return any day.

b.   A belief that Christ could return at any moment should affect our thoughts, for every thought we think could be the last though to pass through our mind before Jesus returns. This, in turn, should affect our speech, for every word that crosses our lips could be the last word we speak before Jesus returns. And this should affect our deeds, for everything we do could be the last thing we do before Jesus returns.

c.   Most of our behavior problems at home and with others would disappear if we lived with the expectation of the Lord's return.

II. INDICATORS THAT POINT TO THE DAY OF THE LORD'S RETURN

Everybody wants to know when the Lord will return. Many people talk about the signs that must be seen before He will return. The truth of the matter is, there are no signs found in the Bible pointing to the "rapture," the first part of Christ's returning.

All the signs found in the Bible were given to the nation of Israel. They point not to the rapture, but to the second coming of Christ as described in Revelation, chapter 19. According to the Bible, the return of Christ (since His departure recorded in Acts 1) has always been imminent! That means it could happen at any time.

If the Lord had given us signs pointing to the rapture, most Christians wouldn't be found serving the Lord with any amount of zeal until the days immediately preceding His return. The Lord wants us to live each day in expectation of His return for us.

We do find several indicators of the conditions in the world in the period of time the Bible calls *the latter days.* The Lord doesn't want us to set dates for His return, but He does want us to learn how to look for the time called the latter days and be more busy in His service as His coming draws closer. Some of the indicators Jesus listed point to the latter days. These signs do not point us to the rapture; they are simply indicators of the conditions of the world in the days near His return. Read II Timothy 3:1-5.

A.   The *moral* indicators.

1.   In II Timothy 3 we find a lengthy list of attitudes and actions that will characterize the latter days. Leading the list in verse 1 is "perilous times."
     a.   This means hazardous and dangerous days.
     b.   Violent crime increases in America every year, often by as much as 30 percent.
     c.   A major crime is committed in our nation every 10 seconds.
     d.   Not only is it dangerous to walk the streets of our major cities in America at night, but

Americans aren't as safe abroad as they once were.

    e.   We live in perilous times.

2.   II Timothy 3:2 lists eight different moral indicators in one verse.

    a.   *"Lovers of self"*—Selfishness and lack of concern for others is one characteristic.

    b.   *"Covetous"*—We live in days when the love and desire for material possessions is wrecking even the lives of many Christians.

    c.   *"Boasters"*—No one wants to buy anything today that doesn't have the right label on it? We are a generation consumed with status symbols.

    d.   *"Proud"*—Pride is resistance toward God. We certainly have a lot of that kind of pride today. People think they have all they need without God.

    e.   *"Blasphemers"*—This means to speak of God in an irreverent manner. The name of Almightly God is not a name that many respect today. God is made the topic of everything from comic movies to commercials.

    f.   *"Disobedience to Parents"*—There has never been any other generation before this one which has witnessed the lack of respect for parents as we do today.

    g.   *"Unthankful"*—We have raised a nation of people today who have little gratitude for the privileges we enjoy in America. It seems the more we have today, the more we want tomorrow.

    h.   *"Unholy"*—There is little left that is holy. We have mocked religion, booted the Bible from any public gathering in school or government, and made light of the traditional values of morality and marriage on television. There is just not much left that is holy to our nation.

3.   II Timothy 3:3 lists six more moral indicators.

    a.   *"Without Natural Affection"*—In the latter days the "natural affection" of a family will be in jeopardy. There are three things that point to this today.

        1.   The first is homosexuality. This is, of course, an unnatural affection. Homosexuality has reached epidemic proportions today.

        2.   Second, is divorce. It hasn't been too many years ago that divorce was almost unheard of, especially in the Christian community. Today, we see the effects of divorce all around us. Divorce is related to this sign of the times. Marriage today,

in many cases, is without the affection that ought to be natural.

3. Finally, we must include abortion. Abortion, just one generation ago, was an unthinkable alternative. It is natural for a mother to love her baby, even in the womb. It is a real lack of natural affection that has brought the abortion crisis to our land. Nearly 4,000 times a day, every day in America, a baby is aborted. This is related to the lack of natural affection listed in the Bible as a sign of the latter days.

b. *"Trucebreakers"*—A trucebreaker is one who fails to keep a promise or a commitment. There was a time in our nation when much business was conducted with nothing more than a handshake to "seal the deal." Those day are over. Today, it seems almost in vogue to scheme and cheat in the name of business.

c. *"False Accusers"*—Slander is something we read everyday in our newspapers and watch nightly on news broadcasts. In many cases it doesn't matter that the story hasn't been verified, as long as it sells. We live in a day of false accusers.

d. *"Incontinent"*—This means uncontrolled living. There is very little moral restraint today. The motto of the last few generations has been, "If it feels good, do it!" What happened to moral control and restraint? Isn't this also a sign of our times?

e. *"Fierce"*—Violence is common in our day. One cannot read the paper without shock and disgust at how brutal and savage mankind can be.

f. *"Despisers of those that are good"*—This refers to the attitudes of many today who have what could be categorized as a hatred for those who try to live right and do good.

5. Four more indicators are listed in verse 4.
   a. *"Traitors"*—This refers to disloyalty. Nearly everyone has suffered at some time under the hand of the disloyal. It may have been an employee or an employer. It may have been a family member or a neighbor. It may have been a trusted friend or church member, but all of us have experienced disloyalty. A lack of loyalty to a cause, a person or ministry is another sign of our times.
   b. *"Heady"*—Headiness is another way of describing one who is headstrong and stubborn, always right, never guilty.
   c. *"Highminded"*—People who are highminded

have inflated egos. The Bible warns us not to think too highly of ourselves. Many people today suffer under the false assumption of their great worth. No one is indispensable to the work of the Lord. We need to put ourselves in the Biblical category of the servant to others, and watch out for the attitude of "highmindedness." The Bible says, *"Let each esteem others better than himself."* Let others think highly of you if they want, but be careful of how highly you think of yourself.

d.   ***"Lovers of Pleasure More Than Lovers of God"***—This really doesn't need a lot of explanation. It means exactly what it says. The evidence is everywhere! Look in most churches on Sunday morning and evening; then look inside the places of amusement. The parks, the beaches, and the lakes are all full, while many churches are "full" of empty pews. We live in days when people worship pleasure and the pursuit of pleasure more than they worship God. The Apostle Paul could have been reading our daily newspapers when he wrote these words centuries ago.

6.   The shocking thing in this passage is, according to II Timothy 3:5 these are the prevailing attitudes of those *"who profess godliness!"* These are the attitudes of professing Christians living in the latter days! If you examine this list carefully you will see how true the Bible is in its description of our day.

B.   The ***"Political and National Indicators"*** (For this portion please refer to Matthew 24 and follow along.)

1.   Politically, the world will be in a stage of unrest in the latter days.
a.   Matthew 24:6 _____

_____

_____

b.   Jesus said, *"Nation shall rise against nation."*
c.   There has never been a time in our history when more nations were at war with one another.

2.   The most outstanding indicator is found in Matthew 24:32-34. It deals with Israel becoming a nation once again.
a.   In His preaching Jesus often used parables to illustrate Bible truths. Whenever Jesus referred to a fig tree in relationship to Israel, He was making a reference to Israel as a nation and as a recognizable power among the nations of the world.
b.   When Jesus spoke the words we read in Matthew 24, Israel wasn't a sovereign nation. It

  was and had been under Roman authority. In verses 32-34 Jesus is, in reality, giving a sign of prophecy! He says, *"When you see Israel become a nation once again you will know that you are living in the latter days."*

  c. Many turn-of-the-century preachers preached from this prophecy and drew only scorn and ridicule. But on May 14th, 1948, Israel did indeed become a sovereign nation once again. Not just a nation, but a respected nation—a nation of power and influence. This truth is one of the greatest indicators of the latter days leading up to the Lord's return.

C. The *Spiritual* indicators that point to the Lord's return

 1. Several of these spiritual indicators are found in Matthew, chapter 24. For instance, verse 5 teaches that a "false Christ" will arise.

  There has never been a day like today with so very many false Christs claiming to be the Messiah. The cults that follow these false Christs are growing at an alarming rate.

 2. Not only false Christs, but also false prophets will preach their seducing doctrines and deceive many. Matthew 24:11 _____

_____

_____

  a. Read I Timothy 4:1. You'll find further proof that false prophets and the spreading of false doctrine is a sign of the latter days.

  b. The number of cults that have their roots in some type of eastern mysticism is growing rapidly.

 3. We find the next spiritual indicator in II Peter 3:3-4, which says that in the latter days there will be scoffers who mock the preaching and teaching of the coming of Christ.

  a. You do not need a pastor or a Bible teacher to inform you that we live in a day and age when very few take seriously the rapture of the Church and the second coming of Christ.

  b. Scoffers can be found in neighborhoods, schools, places of business and even in many churches.

 4. Revelation 3:14-19 teaches that the last days, before the rapture takes place, will be characterized by "spiritual lukewarmness."

  a. This is a lack of consistency—not really hot, and not really cold; up one day, and down the next; on top of the mountain one day and down in the valley the next day.

  b. That is a pretty good illustration of modern

Christianity. This truly is a day of lukewarmness. Many Christians have just enough of the Lord to keep them from really enjoying the world, and just enough of the world to keep them from enjoying the Lord. That's lukewarmness!

5. The most disturbing attitude found in the last days is described in Matthew 24:37-39. Write verse 39.

    _____

    _____

    a. The Bible is not making reference to the sin in the world in Noah's day. Rather, the Bible is talking about the attitude of the people to whom Noah preached.
    b. He preached to people who were filled with apathy. They had no concern!
    c. Noah preached of the judgment of God that was soon to come, and it is as though they said, "I don't care."
        1. Verse 38 tells us they were *"eating, and drinking, marrying and giving in marriage, until the day that Noah entered into the ark."*
        2. Life went on as usual.
        3. They didn't believe Noah's message nor did they heed his warning.
        4. They perished because of unconcern!
    d. Isn't that a picture of the world we live in today? Notice Matthew 24:42 and 44. What do these two verses teach you? _____

        _____

        _____

    e. Be "ye" also ready, for someday the Lord will return.

III. THE JUDGMENT OF THE SAVED AND THE UNSAVED

Many people have the mistaken idea that someday in the future God is going to have one big general judgment of all people who have ever lived. Actually that isn't true.

The Bible tells us of a judgment for the saved and a later judgment for all the unsaved. Christ is the judge for every man. The difference in these two judgments is much like the difference in the judgment in the criminal court and at the county fair. The courtroom judgment hands down punishment for one who is guilty. It is the judgment of the condemned law-breaker. The judgment at the county fair determines rewards. It is the reward to those whose works excel. This is a very limited illustration, but it may help you understand at least the basic difference in the two judgments that are to come.

A.   The judgment for the saved is called *"the judgment seat of Christ."*

   1.   II Corinthians 5:10 teaches that we must all appear before the judgment seat of Christ. (Paul wrote to the Believers at Corinth.)

      a.   We conclude this teaching is extended to Believers only; only Believers will appear at the judgment seat.

      b.   This is not a judgment of sins, but a judgment of each Christian's works.

   2.   Read the basis of this judgment in I Corinthians 3:11-15.

      a.   The wood, hay and stubble represent the temporal things of this world.

         1.   These are not lasting things, yet these are the things for which many labor tirelessly.

         2.   Matthew 6:19 _____

            _____

            _____

      b.   The gold, silver and precious stones represent the eternal things, the things that are precious to the Lord.

         1.   The only eternal work in which we can invest our time, talent and energy is the work of the Lord.

         2.   Only the souls of men, women, teenagers, boys and girls are eternal.

         3.   Let us labor in the work of the Lord so others may be in Heaven with us. This is the closest work to the heart of God.

   3.   I Corinthians 3:14-15 teaches that this judgment is a judgment for rewards (or loss of rewards) and not a judgment upon our sins. For those of us who have put our faith in Christ and been born again, our sins have already been judged at Calvary. Romans 8:1

      _____

      _____

      a.   If you spend your Christian life only in the pursuit of material gain and temporal goods, you can expect to enter Heaven *"yet so as by fire,"* as mentioned in I Corinthians 3:15. People whose houses catch fire may escape the flames, but they find themselves empty-handed.

      b.   How sad it would be for a child of God to live a life too busy to serve the Lord or too busy to witness to a friend, then die and stand before the Lord empty-handed.

      c.   The judgment seat of Christ is a judgment for Believers only. This judgment will determine rewards based on labor rendered in the service of the Lord. Revelation 22:12 _____

_____

_____

B. The last judgment to ever take place is the judgment upon the lost. It is the judgment on all who die without Christ as their Savior. This judgment is called the ***"great white throne"*** of God.

1. It is vividly described in Revelation 20:11-15.

2. The scene of this judgment is found in Revelation 20:11.
   a. John sees a *"great white throne."*
   b. The word *"great"* denotes its authority.
   c. The word *"white"* represents its purity in judgment. God is a righteous judge.
   d. The word *"throne"* speaks of an exalted position. It is a seat of exalted power.
   e. Read Philippians 2:9-11 and write verse 10. ____

   _____

   _____

3. The Savior is the judge.
   a. Revelation 20:11 says, *"and him that sat on it, from whose face the earth and the heaven fled away...."* This is none other than Jesus Himself!
   b. How do we know Jesus is the one who sits in the place of judgment? John 5:22 _____

   _____

   _____

4. The subjects of this judgment are shown in Revelation 20:12.
   a. This is the judgment upon the unsaved dead, "small and great." Rich and poor, educated and uneducated, famous men and common men, young and old, all will stand before the throne of God.
   b. A very descriptive list is found in Revelation 21:8. _____

   _____

   _____

5. The source of judgment is said to be the "books," along with another book, which is called the Book of Life.
   a. According to Revelation 20:13, the dead are judged according to their works as recorded in these books.
   b. This is a judgment to determine degrees of punishment in eternity. Jesus taught this same principle in Matthew 23:14. _____

_____

_____

Jesus warned the Pharisees that they were subject to greater damnation (punishment) because of their ceaseless efforts against the work of God.

c. For those who continually reject the Gospel and spend their lives in sin and wickedness without conscience, hell will hold a severe punishment. This judgment is determined by the works of each individual.

6. The final sentence is passed in Revelation 20:15. ___

_____

a. The Book of Life will be opened as uncontestable proof that each one present at the great white throne judgment died without trusting Christ as Savior.

b. Jesus told us to rejoice because our names are written in the Book of Life. (Luke 10:20) Receiving God's gift of eternal life (given by His grace and received by our faith in His Son) ought to be reason enough for daily rejoicing!

c. Salvation is the most important matter of life. Mark 8:36 _____

_____

7. The seal on this judgment is listed in Revelation 14:11 and Revelation 20:10.

a. There is no parole board in hell; there are no exit doors; there will be no way of escape.

b. Remember, however, God is a God of mercy and grace. It isn't His desire for people to die lost and spend eternity in hell.

1. He cared so very much He sent His only Son, Jesus, to die for the sins of the world.

2. Revelation 22:17 has God's final invitation in the Bible. This is in the last chapter and in the last verses of the Word of God. It's as though God couldn't finish His Book without making one final appeal. He says, _"Whosoever will, let him take of the water of life freely."_

3. May we proclaim that wonderful and simple invitation around the world so others can come to know the Lord Jesus and escape the great white throne of God.

SUMMARY: A certain Bible college used to have what was called, white glove inspections of the men's rooms. These inspections took place any time after a notice had been given. The men never knew the exact day or the exact hour of inspection; they only knew that one would be made soon. It was their duty to have rooms clean and in order, or face the dean of men. But it was easy to put off housecleaning to a later day.

Sometimes the inspector came and someone wasn't prepared. They just simply didn't believe he would show up when he did. Needless to say, they were embarrassed and ashamed. Later they had to face the consequences and give an explanation as to why they hadn't heeded the notice to be ready.

That's a good illustration of the Lord's returning for his own someday. The Bible tells us that Jesus will return. We have been warned that His appearing will be quiet unexpected. Therefore, we must be ready every day. We need not fear the coming of the Lord, but it's important that we live each day expecting His return lest He call us to stand before him when we are unprepared.

The Christian's sins have already been judged on the cross. Our works, however, will someday be brought to light. How wonderful it will be for every saved person when Jesus returns! But how much more wonderful for those who have been busy in the business of the King. *"Watch therefore: for ye know not what hour your Lord doth come."*

REFLECTIONS: Answer the following questions individually or in class. Give careful attention to your answers. This exercise is what the Bible refers to as *meditation.* Think on these things....

1. The return of Christ is divided into two parts. Explain the difference.

   _____

   _____

2. What separates these two parts of the Lord's return? How long of a period of time expires?

   _____

   _____

3. In Acts 1:11 we are told that Jesus will return in *like manner* as he left. What does that mean to you?

   _____

   _____

4. What will be some of the immediate effects of the rapture if that event takes place today?

   _____

   _____

5. For what reason has the Lord set aside the period of time the Bible calls the tribulation?

   _____

   _____

6. Who are the two primary characters that will be in power during the years of the tribulation? How do they differ?

   _____

   _____

7. How should a belief in the imminent appearance of Christ affect one's life?

   _____

   _____

8. List two or three of the moral indicators that point to the period of time the Bible calls the Last Days.

   _____

   _____

9. What prophecy that Jesus listed in Matthew, chapter 24, relating to the latter days have we witnessed since the turn of the century?

   _____

   _____

10. What is the judgment seat of Christ?

    _____

    _____

11. What is the great white throne of God?

    _____

    _____

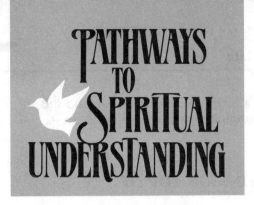

PATHWAYS TO SPIRITUAL UNDERSTANDING

LESSON 18

How to Live the Joy-filled Life

MAIN SCRIPTURES:
PSALM 34; PSALM 71:1-18; MATTHEW 6:24-34;
JUDE 17-25; PROVERB 18:14; PROVERB 17:22

LESSON AIM: To learn how to develop the character of joy and faith that will overcome things like worry and discouragement in the life of a Christian. To lead to a proper understanding of the trials and troubles that come to everyone's life, and to learn a Biblical approach to solving them.

SUGGESTED MEMORY VERSES: Proverb 18:14; Psalm 1:1-2; Isaiah 46:4; Psalm 118:24; Matthew 6:34

OVERVIEW:

I. THE SECRET TO STAYING ON TOP OF CIRCUMSTANCES

II. HOW TO TRIUMPH OVER TROUBLES

III. TO LIVE THE JOY-FILLED LIFE YOU MUST STAY IN LOVE WITH THE LORD

IV. REASONS THE CHRISTIAN SHOULD NEVER WORRY

V. HOW TO GROW BETTER, RATHER THAN BITTER, AS YOU GROW OLDER

INTRODUCTION: There is one thing all people have in common. We all have our own personal trials and troubles while we live here upon the earth. Young or old, wealthy or poor, educated or uneducated, it doesn't matter. Everyone has a certain amount of problems to face while he lives. In Job 5:7 we read, *"Yet man is born unto trouble, as the sparks fly upward."*

Perhaps the author of that verse had watched as an ironsmith lifted his great hammer and allowed it to fall swiftly upon heated metal. When the cold iron of a hammer's head strikes softened metal, sparks fly upward, lighting the sky in a dozen different directions.

It does seem, sometimes, that when troubles fall upon our lives, the sparks fly in so many different directions it's difficult to count them.

Since we cannot promise ourselves lives that are trouble-free, we must learn how to face our problems in such a way that we don't lose the joy of the Lord. It's a sad testimony for a Christian to have joy only when his or her life is in perfect order. We must learn how to live the life of joy, even in the face of trials, if we are ever to be an effective testimony of Christ before others.

How can we face times of adversity and still keep a sweet spirit inside? God's Word holds the key.

195

(Where lines are provided after a Scripture reference, look up the verse and write a one sentence summary of what this Scripture is saying to you.)

I. THE SECRET TO STAYING ON TOP OF CIRCUMSTANCES

Proverbs 18:14 teaches a tremendous principle of life. This verse tells how to stay happy and feel good even when, physically, you may not feel as well as you wish.

A. Guard your spirit faithfully.

   1. The key to keeping joy in your life is to learn to guard your spirit.
       a. Your spirit is the center of your thoughts and emotions.
       b. In the Bible, the words *"spirit"* and *"heart"* are often used interchangeably.
       c. The spirit (or heart) of a man motivates all he does.
       d. All actions begin in our hearts as we contemplate what we are going to say or do.
       e. Our attitudes, moods and temperaments are determined in our spirit. Read Matthew 15:18-20.
       f. Proverb 18:14 actually teaches that it is possible to be physically sick, yet recover quickly because of a strong spirit.
       g. You may have a headache, a backache, broken leg or ulcers, but a strong spirit will take you through these times with joy still in your heart.
       h. It's easy to be joyful when the sky is blue and no troubles appear; it is another thing to be joyful when problems arise.
       i. If you are ever to learn to live the life of a victorious Christian, you must first learn more about keeping (or guarding) your heart with all diligence.

   2. A wounded spirit is a difficult thing to bear.
       a. The spirit is the healer of the body. When the spirit is injured or wounded there is a serious problem.
       b. The best medicine for the spirit is preventative medicine. It's better to learn how to guard your spirit in order to keep it from ever being injured, than to have to heal it once it has been injured. Proverb 17:22 _____

       _____

       _____

       c. You must learn to stand guard just like a sentry at the door of your heart.
       d. When you feel the enemies of your spirit

about to creep in, you must slam the door.

1. Things like hurt feelings, criticism, self-pity, bad attitudes, slander, complaining, discouragement, and a host of other enemies must be stopped before they attack your heart and do great harm and damage.

2. When you feel these seeking a grip on your heart you must stop and pray for the Lord's help to fight these destructive devices.

3. Learn to hide Scripture away in your heart so that it can be called upon to help you in this battle.

4. Psalm 119:11 _____

_____

_____

e. There is nothing better for your life than a "merry heart." Proverb 17:22 _____

_____

_____

3. Consider a few Bible examples.

a. Job lost more than most of us will ever lose. His lost his wealth, his health, and his children. Even his so-called friends turned against him. Yet Job kept hold on the reins of his heart and continued to believe God would bring him through his time of trouble. Job 13:15 _____

_____

_____

If you read the last chapter of the book of Job you will see how God blessed him after he endured his troubles.

b. Moses was a great leader, and a man of faith; but there came a day when he became frustrated with the people he was called to lead.

1. God told him to speak to a rock in the wilderness. Instead, he stuck the rock in anger.

2. Because he lost control of his spirit, God could no longer use Moses to the same extent.

3. In fact, because of this sin Moses wasn't allowed to cross into the promised land. This story is recorded in Numbers, chapter 20.

c. Many of God's best servants never recovered after sustaining a wounded spirit. How much better it is to learn how to guard the heart and keep it from evil injury. Read Proverbs 4:20-23.

Write verse 23. _____

_____

_____

4.   If you are to guard your heart, you must learn to avoid scorners.

a.   Wounded spirits seem to attract each other. Be careful about those you fellowship with, for their attitudes and temperaments may rub off on you! Proverb 13:20 _____

_____

_____

b.   You can always recognize a scorner by the words he speaks.
1.   The Bible teaches that there is a direct link between the heart and mouth. Matthew 12:34 _____

_____

_____

2.   When a man's heart isn't right, his mouth will give him away.
3.   The Bible teaches us to avoid those who are in the business of causing offense. Romans 16:17 _____

_____

_____

B.   To aid further in the endeavor of guarding your heart you must stay occupied in doing good.

1.   Keep your heart, mind, hand and mouth busy doing what is good and you will probably never develop a bitter spirit.
a.   It was said of Jesus that He went about doing good.
b.   Every Christian ought to be accused of the same thing.

2.   The Apostle Paul warned that idleness leads to other sins.
a.   I Timothy 5:13 _____

_____

_____

(Read also II Thessalonians 3:11-13.)
b.   II Thessalonians 3:13 gives the key to this whole discussion. *"Don't grow weary in well doing."* That's the secret! that's what adds health and strength to your spirit. Keep busy doing good.

C.   Stay close to the Lord Jesus.

1. Develop a close and personal relationship with the Lord. Make Him your best friend.
    a. This is perhaps the very best medicine for your heart.
    b. To develop a closer walk with the Lord, you must spend time in the Bible. It's in the pages of the ***written word*** that you learn more of the ***living Word.***
    c. To develop a closer relationship with the Lord, you must also spend more a time in prayer than the average Christian does.
    d. When you learn to spend some time each day with your Bible and on your knees in prayer, it won't be long until you feel as though the Lord's presence is with you every moment of every day.

2. Stay close to your Bible.

    a. Psalm 119:165 _____

    _____

    _____

    b. When you walk in the Word of God, your heart develops a protective coating. (Not physically of course, but spiritually.) There isn't much that will offend the Christian who places his trust in the promises of God's Word. Read Psalm 1:1-3. Write the lessons you learn. _

    _____

    _____

    c. Christians frequently grow cold, critical and miserable when they begin to neglect their Bibles.

II. HOW TO TRIUMPH OVER TROUBLES

This is principle number one—trouble is common to everyone. If you fail to realize that everyone has some trouble come his way, you'll grow discouraged. Once you know that principle, it's important to learn how to turn times of trouble into times of triumph. In order to do this, it's necessary to understand how to meet troubles when they arrive.

A. You must meet the Person who can help you overcome life's troubles.

1. No one is ready to meet trouble until he first knows Christ as his Savior. One needs to know Christ and have the assurance of salvation before he is fully able to face trouble and triumph.

    Jesus is the only One who is perfectly able to share burdens and help lift every load of life. Matthew 11:28 _____

    _____

    _____

2. People usually face their problems in one of several ways.

    a. Some people face them with anger. They get mad at God and everyone else, just like the children of Israel got mad at God and complained about Moses when they were hungry in the wilderness. This is never an acceptable way for a Christain to face problems.

    b. Some meet their problems with self-pity. They withdraw inside themselves and wallow in despair. Elijah did this when Jezebel threatened his life. Many Christians look for the closest "juniper tree" when troubles comes. This is also not an acceptable way to face trouble.

    c. Some meet trouble with worry and anxiety. They lose sleep and refuse to eat or enjoy anyone's company because they're so consumed with worry. Worry is never proper for the Christian.

    d. Other people meet their problems with faith in God's ability to help them through. This is the proper attitude for the child of God.

B. Meet your problem without delay.

1. Don't manufacture problems for yourself. Don't make them worse than they already are.

    a. The wisest thing you can do is to look in the Bible and learn how to avoid trouble.

    b. You will have enough trouble in life without making any extra for yourself.

    c. Read Psalm 34:12-14. Verse 12 asks who wants to see good and enjoy life. The answer follows in verses 13 and 14. What are the things one must do, according to this Scripture? _____

_____

_____

    d. Our eyes and our mouths often lead us into trouble. Read Proverb 4:25-27. Write Psalm 101:3 _____

_____

_____

    e. Read Proverb 21:23 and write the lesson taught in this verse. _____

_____

_____

2. Don't ignore your troubles or run from them.

    a. There are lessons to be learned from the problems that we face. If we look, we can always find a learning situation in every trial and in every trouble.

    b.   By ignoring problems they only grow larger. We must learn to face them as soon as they appear.

C.   Meet your problems with a plan.

   When problems arise there are only a few things you can do.

   1.   You can complain about them. This of course, doesn't help solve them and may ruin your testimony.

   2.   You can pity yourself and try to convince yourself that you must simply bear your problem like some kind of heavy burden. If this is your attitude, you're going to miss any blessing that God could give you through your trial.

   3.   You can blame others, as did Adam and Eve. This will only lead you to be separated and divided against the ones who love you.

   4.   Or...you can meet your problems with a prescribed plan already firmly set in your mind.

     a.   Part of this plan involves prayer. Take your troubles to God's throne in prayer!

       1.   Read Philippians 4:6-7. What does this passage teach? _____

                      _____

                      _____

       2.   Write Hebrews 4:16. _____

                      _____

                      _____

       3.   You cannot do anything more until you have prayed.

     b.   Another part of your plan should involve looking for the blessings that accompany trouble.

       1.   Trouble can draw us closer to God or even closer together as a family.

       2.   Trouble can also move us into a place where God wants to use us.

       3.   Trouble can move us into the place of God's blessing. Read the story of Joseph in Egypt, found in Genesis 37:20 through Genesis 45:15. Write Genesis 45:7. _____

                      _____

                      _____

       4.   Learn to look for the lessons hidden in the troubles that come across your path.

     c.   Trouble can teach the ministry of compassion for others. It's difficult to know how to help bear the burdens of others if we have never carried any ourselves. Read II Corinthians

1:3-4. What does this passage of Scripture teach? _____

_____

_____

    d.   We must learn to rest in the power and the promises of God when we face times of trouble. When we trust, we don't worry; when we worry, we don't trust. Learn to trust God by faith. Psalm 34:19 _____

_____

_____

Find comfort and help in passages like Psalm 40:1-4. God loves us as a father loves his children. Learn to rest in His love and trust Him to bring you safely through your afflictions.

III. TO LIVE THE JOY-FILLED LIFE YOU MUST STAY IN LOVE WITH THE LORD.

Weddings are wonderful! Each year thousands of couples take their vows of marriage. The only thing is, after every wedding comes the marriage. In the early days of a marriage a lot of joy, a lot of excitement and a lot of love is shown. But in order to keep the flame of love burning brightly, it is necessary to keep that "first love" alive.

It's like that in the Christian life also. We need to keep our "first love" for the Lord and for the things of the Lord. Read Jude, verses 17-25. Look carefully at the first part of verse 21. *"Keep yourselves in the love of God...."* If you are going to live the life of joy, not only must you learn how to guard your heart and overcome trouble, but you must also learn how to remain in love with the Lord. It isn't the pastor's job to keep you in love with God. The Bible says, *"keep **yourselves** in the love of God."*

Many Christians today have fallen out of love with the Lord. They've lost the joy they once had and have grown cold and indifferent to the things of the Lord. This doesn't happen overnight; it happens over a period of time. The device that causes us to leave our first love for God is neglect. When you stop loving the Lord as you once did, it will have a drastic effect upon your life and upon those whose lives are touched by yours. It's imperative, therefore, that you *"keep yourself in the love of God.!"* How can you do that? Four suggestions follow:

A.   Keep yourself in the Word of God.

    1.   This has already been mentioned briefly but it is so vital and so important it must be mentioned again.

        a.   The Bible is the source of spiritual nourishment for every Christian. It's our source of strength!

        b.   To stay spiritually healthy we must exercise ourselves daily in the Bible.

2. There is another reason the Bible is so vital to our relationship with God. Amos 3:3 says, *"Can two walk together except they be agreed?"*
   a. In order to walk with God you must agree with God. How can you agree with God if you don't read His Word and know what He says? Therefore, you can have no lasting relationship with the Lord unless you have a daily relationship with the Word of God.
   b. Every Christian needs to read the Bible, study the Bible, memorize the Bible and attend a church where the Bible is taught and preached. This is vital to his ability to stay in love with the Lord!

B. Keep yourself in the House of God.

1. God has raised up the Church in this generation for two primary purposes.
   a. The Church is to engage in worldwide evangelism. A lot of Church-related problems would disappear if Christians invested more time in evangelism.
   b. The Church is also to exhort and edify the saved. God commanded in Hebrews 10:25 that we not *"forsake the assembling of ourselves together."* Assembling together in church is for our benefit. We need the fellowship of other Christians and we need a place to serve.

2. Another purpose for the Church is found in Ecclesiastes 4:9-12.
   a. Sooner or later we all need someone to help lift us up a little. That's why the Bible says, *"Two are better than one."*
   b. A Christian separated from a good church home is easy prey for the devil. There is strength in numbers! Ecclesiastes 4:12 _____

   _____

   _____

C. Keep in touch with God through prayer.

1. All the great men of the Bible were also great men of prayer. Elijah, Daniel, John, Paul and dozens of others were great in their faith and great in their works because they were great in their prayers.

2. God speaks to us through the Holy Spirit and through the Bible. It is through prayer that we speak with God!
   a. We have direct access to Him any time, any day. No wonder the Bible says, *"Pray without ceasing."*
   b. If you don't find a regular time to talk with the Lord in prayer, your relationship with Him will soon grow stale.

    1.   This same principle holds true in our relationships with others.

    2.   It's impossible to build a loving and growing relationship by long distance.

    3.   We must communicate regularly to build our relationship with others and with the Lord.

  c. Abraham was called *"the friend of God."* Perhaps the reason he enjoyed such a sweet and close relationship with God was due to what we read in Genesis 19:27.

    1.   Evidently Abraham had a special place and a special time set aside for the purpose of talking with God.

    2.   You will not keep yourself in the love of God unless you keep yourself in touch with God through prayer.

D. Keep yourself in the will of God.

  1. There are two parts to the will of God.

    a. First, there is God's ***directive will.***

      1. This is what God desires of every Christian.

      2. The Bible offers guidelines for the Christian to follow. God wants His children to attend church and participate in the acts of baptism, giving, serving, and witnessing outside the church community.

      3. This is God's directive will for all Christians.

    b. There is God's ***selective will.***

      1. This is the purpose He has mapped out for each individual's life.

      2. The will of God for one person's life is not the same will of God for another person's life.

      3. God has a selective will for you. It represents His will for your life alone and is the purpose for which you became a Christian.

    c. If you are to enjoy life to the fullest you need to be concerned about the will of God. No life is quite as joyful as the life of the one who is saved and living in the will of God.

    d. What is God's will for your life? Have you thought about the skills and abilities He has given you? Each of us has some duty we can do for the Lord. You must pray and seek God's leadership concerning His will for your life. This will help you *"keep yourself in the love of God."*

IV. REASONS THE CHRISTIAN SHOULD NEVER WORRY

Worry is one of the most common sins among Christians. Many people fail to see worry as a sin, but it's the sin of not trusting God. No one can possibly live a joy-filled life unless he learns how to deal with this device of the devil. The devil uses worry as a wrench, to twist our heads away from God. He robs us of sleep, peace, faith and joy with nothing more than worry. Read Matthew 6:24-37.

A. Worry always accomplishes nothing.

    1. Worry is the supreme waste of time.

        a. Matthew 6:27 asks a very good question. *"Which of you by taking thought (worrying) can add one cubit unto his stature?"*

        b. If you're 4' 10", worrying about being short will not add an inch to your size.

        c. Time is far too precious to waste it on the worthless endeavor of worry.

    2. How many problems have you solved by worrying?

        a. Worrying about a problem never leads to a solution.

        b. Worry is a foolish waste of valuable time. If you value the preciousness of time, convince yourself not to waste time in an activity which accomplishes nothing.

B. Worry afflicts the body with illness.

    1. It isn't a theory; it's a fact! Worrying on a regular basis will take years off your life. It leads to headaches, stress, poor digestion and a loss of sleep, to name just a few of the results of worry on the body.

    2. A Christian doesn't have the right to treat his or her body in this manner.

        a. Your body is the temple (dwelling place) of the Holy Spirit. I Corinthians 6:19 _____

        _____

        _____

        b. The body of one who is saved belongs to the Lord. Would you intentionally mistreat the place where God dwells? If you persist in worrying, that's exactly what you're doing. Worry is harmful to the body.

C. Worry affects the spirit.

    1. Not only does the body of a Christian belong to God, so does the spirit.

        a. According to I Corinthians 6:19-20 the Christian is to bring glory to God both in his body and in his spirit.

        b. Does it glorify God to worry and become depressed in spirit? Of course not.

205

2.   Christians are Christ's ambassadors to the rest of the world.
     a.   Worry always shows up whether in facial expressions or in attitudes.
     b.   How can you be a good representative of the Lord, whom you are to love and trust, if you spend your days worrying?
     c.   Worry causes spiritual bitterness, harshness and discouragement.

D.   Worry keeps you from serving God.

1.   There is no way one can effectively serve God without trusting Him.
     a.   By making you worry, the devil causes you to take your eyes off of the Lord and away from your task.
     b.   Worry is nothing more than the devil's detour.
     c.   God cannot use one who is filled with worries, for worrying demonstrates a lack of faith and confidence in God.

2.   Read Proverbs 3:5-6. Notice, Christians are to *"trust in the Lord with all thine heart."*
     a.   Does that sound like worry?
     b.   Look at Proverb 3:6. Write its lessons. _____

     _____

     _____

E.   Worry is direct disobedience to the Bible. Read Philippians 3:13-14.

1.   Don't worry over the past.
     a.   Forget the things which are behind. It is useless to worry over that which is past.
     b.   Give the past to the Lord. If you have sinned in the past, seek God's forgiveness and praise Him for the fact that once He forgives sins He also forgets them forever.
     c.   If you dwell too much on the past you won't be effective in the present.

2.   Don't worry about the present.
     a.   Philippians 4:4-7 says, *"Be anxious for nothing...."* That's a very simple way of saying, *"Don't worry about anything."*
     b.   Don't let your life be filled with anxiety over the present. God is still God, and God is still in control of your world.
     c.   When you worry you disobey Philippians 4:7.

3.   Don't worry about the future.
     a.   Matthew 6:34 holds one of the best pieces of advice found in the Bible. _____

     _____

     _____

b.   In this verse Jesus says to take life the way it comes. That is, only live one day at a time.
1.   You cannot change tomorrow by worrying.
2.   Trust God for today and when tomorrow comes trust God again for another day.

c.   Live in 24 hour increments. How much better it would be to turn worry time into prayer time and learn to trust the Lord one day at a time!

d.   I Peter 5:7 teaches what to do with cares and worries. _____

_____

_____

e.   Only by learning to cast your cares upon the Lord, will you conquer worry. And, only by conquering worry will you learn to live a joy-filled life.

V.   HOW TO GROW BETTER, RATHER THAN BITTER, AS YOU GROW OLDER

Read Psalm 90:9. This verse tells how quickly life passes by. Everyone needs to take the time to learn how to grow old joyfully, because all of us grow older every day. Someone many years ago said, "If you dread growing old, just thing of the alternative!"

The senior years of a Christian's life can be some of the best and most productive. Don't allow the devil to steal your joy just because you are no longer in the ranks of the youth. Determine to grow better, not bitter.

A.   Actively cultivate your Christian faith.

1.   The older we grow the more faith we are going to need.
a.   As the flesh grows older it is important for the spirit to grow stronger.
b.   There are burdens and difficulties connected with old age that young people know nothing about.
c.   As we grow older we will need a greater measure of daily faith in the Lord.

2.   The only way to cultivate that faith is through a good program of daily devotions.
a.   Remember, *"faith cometh by hearing and hearing by the Word of God."* (Romans 10:17)
b.   Take advantage of the increased free time many older folks have and spend a little more time in Bible study and in prayer.
c.   We will need to walk a little closer to the Lord the older we grow.

B.   Keep a love in your heart for others.

1.   Read John 15:11-12. The Lord has commanded that we love one another.

    a.   This love for others will keep our own hearts full of the Lord's love.

    b.   It is extremely difficult to grow old joyfully as long as you harbor bitterness against others.

    c.   Be a friend to others as you grow older. That is the way to have friends. You will find an increased need for good friends as you get older. Proverb 18:24 _____

_____

_____

    d.   Some of the warmest, most friendly people in our churches are senior citizens.

C.   Maintain a cheerful spirit each day.

    1.   Learn to greet each day with Psalm 118:24. _____

_____

_____

    a.   You can find something to be thankful for and something for which you can praise the Lord every day of your life.

    b.   Don't grow old with a mean, cranky, complaining spirit. Learn to look for the blessing of the Lord each and every day. If you look, you'll surely find a blessing in every day the Lord gives.

    c.   Develop the type of attitude and spirit as you grow older that makes others want to be around you.

D.   Don't mourn your past.

    1.   Most of us have things in our past that we would like to go back and change.

       a.   Since this is impossible, we must turn loose of the past and live in the present.

       b.   Multitudes of older folks don't live a life of joy because of their inability to let the past go. Memories can be sweet or they can be bitter, but they cannot be changed.

    2.   a.   Learn to start fresh with God each new morning. Seize every opportunity to do good and to enjoy life. Don't let the past steal the enjoyment and sweetness of the present from you as you grow older.

       b.   Trust God each day for His blessing and help for that day. There is an increasing temptation to worry more about daily strength and provision as one grows older. But the God of the young is also the God of the old. Isaiah 46:4 _____

_____

_____

E. Stay busy serving the Lord.

    1. Don't let the devil fool you into believing you should retire from active duty for the Lord at age 60.

        a. Some of the best workers in the church are those who are senior citizens.

        b. Read Psalm 92:13-14. What does this passage say to you? _____

        _____

        _____

        c. As our eyes grow dim and our feet grow a little unsteady, we may have to accept some limitations, but we do not have to stop serving the Lord. The way to keep the joy of the Lord and to keep problems off our minds is to stay busy in the Lord's work.

F. Live each day with the expectancy of the Lord's return.

    1. The last lesson covered what the Bible says about the Lord's return. Without doubt, Jesus is going to return to take believers to Heaven.

        a. That event is called "the rapture" of the Church and is described in I Thessalonians 4:13-18.

        b. If you want to live a joy-filled life you need to expect the Lord's return at any moment! Looking for the undertaker will make you morbid. Looking for the "uppertaker" (Jesus), will make you joyful as you face each day.

        c. When Jesus returns, the things of this life related to heartache and hardships will all be passed. The Bible says in Revelation 21:4, *"...for the former things are passed away."* There will be no more crying, no death, no sorrow, no burdens, no suffering, no problems to bear, no pain to endure. No wonder the Bible teaches the blessedness of this day for all who are saved!

        d. Expect Jesus everyday. It will change the way you feel and the way you live.

SUMMARY: Life is to be lived until Jesus either returns for all Christians or calls each of us to Heaven through death. The Christian is to enjoy life rather than just endure it. Jesus said He came to bring life, and to bring it abundantly. The life of one who has trusted Christ as Savior should be more abundant than the life of those who don't know Christ as Savior. Yet, many who claim to be Christians don't find much joy and contentment. We need to learn to replace the defeated life with the dynamic life! If any group of people living today has cause to rejoice, it's those who have been given the gift of eternal life through the grace of God. May God help each of us understand the precious value of a day and put within us a Godly determination to live each day fully and

to the glory of God. We are on our way to Heaven. We ought to
be enjoying the trip!

PARKED BENEATH A PITY TREE

I found a tree one gloomy day
and leaned against its bark.
The joy of life had disappeared,
my path through life turned dark.

Its branches spread down over me
and closed out all the light.
And there I grumbled in self-pity
although I knew it wasn't right.

Its leaves soon closed out all the world
beneath my tree of "I don't care."
And there will always be a doubter's tree
for those who wallow in despair.

So here beneath a pity tree
I find myself again.
Do you suppose it could be true
that to Elijah I am kin?

For tho' he called down fire from heaven
and reached up to the throne of Grace,
he too, stumbled on the path of pity
and fell discouraged on his face.

Till in a cave he came to lodge
and prayed that he might die.
But the God whom he had loved and served
was listening to him cry.

And with great love the Father came
in a voice so still and small.
He said, "Elijah, I still am here.
Why did you not just call?

"Don't you know I love you?
And you're not alone in serving me.
I have seven thousand others
who have never bowed their knees!"

So before you find yourself a tree,
a place where you can cry,
look up to the Heavens
for God is ever nigh!

And when you feel discouraged
and you're about to quit the fight,
remember God is speaking
if you'll listen and be quiet.

For there is no problem He can't solve,
no child He will not see,
save only those who hide from Him
beneath a "pity tree!"

Dr. Richard S. Powers

REFLECTIONS: Answer the following questions individually or in class. Give careful attention to your answers. This exercise is what the Bible refers to as meditation. Think on these things....

1. What vital principle is taught in Proverb 18:14?

   _____

   _____

2. How could Job endure all the trials of life that came to him in a short period of time?

   _____

   _____

3. Why is it important to avoid scorners?

   _____

   _____

4. What are some of the ways people face their problems? What is the way a Christian ought to face them?

   _____

   _____

5. When faced with problems it is important to have a plan of defense ready. What elements make up your plan?

   _____

   _____

6. What does it mean in the Book of Jude verse 21, *"Keep yourselves in the love of God."*?

   _____

   _____

7. What are the two parts of the will of God?

   _____

   _____

8. Why should a Christian not spend time worrying?

   _____

   _____

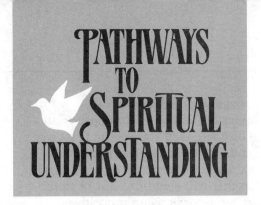

LESSON 19

The Family Life of a Believer

MAIN SCRIPTURES:
PSALM 78:1-8; MARK 10:1-9;
EPHESIANS 5:19-33; EPHESIANS 6:1-4

LESSON AIM: To lead to an understanding of the principles of God's Word concerning marriage and homelife. To learn how the faithful application of these principles will bring about God's blessing to the home. To learn how to keep marriage fresh and growing in love and in joy.

SUGGESTED MEMORY VERSES: Proverb 22:6; Ephesians 6:4; Ephesians 5:25; Proverb 31:10-12

OVERVIEW:

    I. IS YOURS A MARRIAGE MADE IN HEAVEN?

    II. CHILDREN: DELINQUENTS OR DELIGHTS?

    III. HOW TO MAINTAIN A HAPPY MARRIAGE

    IV. AVOIDING THE TRAP OF ADULTERY

    V. WHAT TO DO IF YOUR MARRIAGE IS ALREADY IN TROUBLE

INTRODUCTION: A young man was driving along in his brand new, expensive sports car when another vehicle ran through the intersection and collided with him. His new car was completely demolished and he sustained a broken arm and leg in the crash.

As he lay by the roadside waiting to be lifted into a nearby ambulance, a police officer approached and said, "I know you must be in a lot of pain but I must ask you a few questions." When the young man nodded his approval the policeman asked, "Are you married?" To this the bruised and battered young man replied, "Oh no sir! This is the worst mess I've ever been in."

For millions of married people, that poor fellow and his story summarize the condition of their marriages. Too many married people, including Christians, find themselves in a real mess at home. A large part of the ministry now consists of counseling married couples. Clinics all over the country specialize in Christian marriage counseling. This alone is enough to make us realize that marriage-threatening problems plague not only the homes of those who don't know Christ, but also the homes of Christians.

The devil has launched an all out attack against our homes, our marriages and our children. We must learn what the Bible says about how to achieve success in marriage, and practice those teachings faithfully. Marriage can be one of the sweetest, most wonderful things on earth, or marriage can be one of the most miserable things on earth. The choice is made by each husband and each wife. Marriage is like a bank account. One can only expect to get out of marriage what he puts into it.

God is the designer and the builder of the home. He began it all with Adam and Eve in the garden of Eden. God started the first home with a plan. We must find and follow God's plan. How can you have a home that is filled with joy and the peace of God? How can you build a loving relationship that will stand the test of time? How can you find success in marriage in days when more than half are failing?

(Where lines are provided after a Scripture reference, look up the verse and write a one sentence summary of what this Scripture is saying to you.)

I.   IS YOURS A MARRIAGE MADE IN HEAVEN?

Mark 10:1-9 lists four good, solid principles of Jesus, related to marriage. These make up God's basic guidelines for the home.

A.   Marriage is God's only approved plan for the establishment of the home.

   1.   From the very beginning of creation, marriage was part of the plan of God.
      a.   Mark 10:6 _____

      _____

      _____

      b.   The marriage of one man to one woman was God's plan, as He demonstrated in His creation of the first home.

   2.   We must teach this principle to our children in the home to counter the humanistic teaching that allows a man and a woman to live together without the bond of marriage.
      a.   God's Word is very clear concerning any other arrangement of living together.
      b.   Hebrews 13:4 _____

      _____

      _____

   3.   Since marriage is a relationship approved by God, we must also be certain that our marriage partner is the one approved by God.
      a.   Many people choose a new automobile with more thought and concern than they choose their spouse.
      b.   Perhaps this is the reason for the high rate of divorce in America.
      c.   A very basic, Scripture truth relating to this choice is found in II Corinthians 6:14 _____

      _____

      _____

      d.   The Church should teach young people the

importance of Christians dating Christians.

1. It is wonderful to see our young people witnessing to and bringing the unsaved to youth activities at church.
2. However, dating between the saved and the unsaved is a risky practice.
3. Eventually one will fall in love with someone he dates.
4. If that person happens to be unsaved, they will have a very difficult time with II Corinthians 6:14 when it comes to marriage.
5. This may sound very narrow, but this principle in God's Word is for our happiness and welfare in the future.

   e. We must seek God's approval and leading when it comes to the one we are to marry. God will lead if He is included in the choice. Many people who go to see a pastor about a wedding have never prayed about the choice they are making.
   f. Remember, Samson's troubles began when he decided to marry a Philistine girl rather than an Israelite. (Judges 14:1-7)

B. God intended marriage to be a lifelong relationship between one man and one woman.

1. Foundational to a proper, Biblical understanding of marriage is the truth found in Mark 10:9.
   a. God's intention is that marriage last until the bond is broken by death.
   b. What does *"What God hath joined together..."* mean to you? _____

   _____

   _____

2. Marriage vows are made to God and are some of the most serious promises ever made.
   a. Every Christian husband and wife should occasionally renew their promise to God concerning their marriage vows.
   b. Mention your sacred promise to God and ask His divine help in living up to what you promised Him the day you were married.
   c. Divorce should be a word that is never mentioned in Christian homes.

C. Although divorce is a traumatic event in one's life, some of the best workers are those who, at some time in their past, suffered through a divorce.

1. Divorce is always a hurtful and painful experience. Everyone who is divorced has a story of heartbreak.

2. Divorce was never part of God's plan for our homes. If you are married today you must not view

divorce as an option in a Christian marriage.

3. God's power is available to help Christian couples overcome any problem that may plague their homes.

4. Those who are already divorced must not live in the past and allow the devil to rob them of a life of joy and service to the Lord.
    a. We must learn from past mistakes, but we are not doomed to live miserable or useless lives because of them.
    b. I John 1:9 promises God's complete forgiveness for sins and allows the Christian to live a life unburdened by guilt.

5. Those who are divorced and contemplating marriage again must seek good, competent, pastoral counsel to help guide them in this decision.
    a. It's more heartbreaking and painful to suffer through divorce the second time.
    b. Remember, *"In the multitude of counselors there is safety."* (Proverb 11:14)

D. God planned marriage to be a relationship of joy. happiness and sweetness of unity.

1. According to Mark 10:7 there is no other human relationship as close as the marriage of a man and a woman.
    a. This is the only relationship in which God sees two people as one person.
    b. That is a great mystery, but nevertheless very true! God sees a husband and wife as only one person in the bond of marriage. Unity is the desired goal of every marriage.

2. Notice two important words found in Mark 10:8
    a. The first is the word "leave." A man is to leave his father and mother.
        1. Couples should not take the step of marriage until they are able to leave home and be on their own.
        2. This is important to the success of a young married couple just starting out together.
    b. The second word is "cleave." This means a husband and wife are to mold their lives around one another in such fashion that nothing can divide them.
        1. The reason for so many divorces today is that most divorced couples never achieved this "oneness."
        2. It only takes small things to divide couples that don't learn how to "cleave" to one another.

3. Unity can only be achieved when each spouse fulfills the role God has given him.

a.   There is no lasting joy until husband and wife assume their God-given obligations and responsibilities.

b.   Rebellion against this principle leads to unhappiness and ultimately to failure.

4.   The husband's duty is found simply, yet wonderfully outlined in Ephesians 5:25. _____

_____

_____

a.   Every husband is bound by God to display a love for his wife equal to the love Christ displayed for His Church.

b.   This is a great command for men.

1.   It means that a husband is to love his wife with a sacrificial love, a patient love, a serving love, a giving love, a kind love, a forgiving love and a passionate love.

2.   It means he is to study the life of Christ and endeavor to treat his wife just as Jesus would! How many husbands have ever thought of this as their duty?

c.   A husband is to love his wife with an "unconditional" love. He is to love her regardless of her treatment of him.

1.   We are not to love only for what we can get out of a relationship.

2.   We are to love as Christ loved; He has commanded it.

3.   Every husband is to love his wife as a matter of obedience to the Lord.

4.   God would never command you to do what He will not teach you to do.

5.   Christian husbands should pray daily for God's wisdom and help in learning how to love their wives as God wants them to.

5.   The wife's obligation to her husband is found in Ephesians 5:22-24.

a.   Write verse 22. _____

_____

_____

b.   Many women have grown to resent the preaching, and teaching of this verse because they don't really understand what it says.

1.   Submission has nothing to do with matters of superiority and inferiority.

2.   Submission means "to place beneath."

3.   A wife must place herself under her husband's headship for the purpose of supporting him.

4.   Anything with two heads is unnatural; it cannot survive.

5.   God put the husband in the position of

being the "head' of the home. (This principle is found in Ephesians 5:23).

    6.   His position as head is not for his own benefit, rather for the benefit of his family.

    7.   He will someday answer to God for the way he ruled over his home or for his failure to do so.

  c. The type of submission taught in the Bible is illustrated quite easily in the foundation of a building.

    1.   The foundation of a building is under the building itself.

    2.   We could say it is "submitting" to the building, but the foundation is there to uphold and support the building.

    3.   Likewise, a wife is to submit to her husband's God-given authority as the head of the home; but her position is one of support and encouragement.

    4.   As no building can stand without a solid foundation, no home will stand in joy and peace without a Godly wife who upholds and supports her husband.

    5.   Husbands should remember that their position is one of Christlikeness to the other members of the household.

  d. The husband's role in the home is different from the wife's role, but neither can function properly without the other. There is no competition or selfishness or resentment in the lives of those who walk in unity.

E.   God planned marriage to be a spiritual relationship.

  1. Again, in Mark 10:9 we read, *"What therefore God hath joined together...."*

    a. The very institution of marriage is a spiritual union and an act of almighty God.

    b. It isn't the pastor who joins two people in marriage. It isn't even the state that unites two people in marriage. It's God!

    c. There is little hope of achieving lasting joy in marriage for those who don't pursue spiritual things at home.

  2. Jesus illustrated this principle in a story found in Luke 6:47-49. It's the story of two men who built houses on two different types of foundations.

    a. One man's home was built upon a rock. Jesus said that when the storms of life came his house stood because of its good foundation.

    b. The other man built his house upon the sand. He had no secure foundation, and when the storms arrived, his house fell.

    c. The first man is likened to a man who not

only hears the Word of God, but sets out to do whatever God's Word commands. The house built upon the Bible and its principles will be able to withstand the storm.

d. The foolish man endeavored to build without the foundation of the Bible. He represents a "hearer" of the Word, but not a "doer." He had no secure foundation, and when the storms came, his house collapsed.

e. It's important to understand that the storms came to both homes. Building a home upon the principles of the Bible will not exempt anyone from life's storms, but it most certainly will help the home stand when storms come!

f. Every week someone's home falls apart. Most of these people have simply neglected the Bible and spiritual things. They have tried to build upon the shifting sands of materialism and other such things. How important it is to build a marriage and home upon the sound and solid principles found in the Bible!

g. If marriage is to withstand the test of time it must have a spiritual foundation upon which to rest. Christ needs to be the Head of the home. His Word ought to be your guide and counselor. This foundation will last when the storms arrive.

II. CHILDREN: DELINQUENTS OR DELIGHTS?

Read Psalm 78:1-8. This Psalm teaches how to instruct children in the things of the Lord. One the greatest obligations God has ever given is that of raising children. It seems that each generation fails just a little more than the previous generation in meeting the needs of children. Parents have allowed themselves to grow much more concerned over the material needs (or wants) of their children than the things which are true needs. What are the things children need that parents should supply?

A. Today's children need someone who will defend their right to live.

1. Unborn babies are now aborted at the rate of one and one-half million each year. Someone in our generation must stand up in defense of our country's most defenseless citizen—the unborn child!

2. Read Psalm 139:13-16. God considered us, in our mother's womb, as complete a human being as we will ever be.

a. The New Testament uses the very same word for a baby in the womb and a baby which has already been born.

b. Read the story of Mary's visit to her cousin Elisabeth, recorded in Luke 1:39-45. What does Elisabeth say in verse 44? _____

_____

_____

    c.   The word "babe" is the exact word used in Luke 2:16 to describe the baby Jesus laying in the manger. God uses only one word to describe a baby, whether in the womb or out of the womb, for He knows both are little human beings.

        1.   There is no word in all the Bible that corresponds with the word "fetus."

        2.   We must understand this Bible truth in order to counter the philosophy of humanism which promotes the idea that an unborn child isn't really a human being.

        3.   According to the Bible, this teaching is totally in error!

    d.   God makes absolutely no distinction between an unborn infant and a baby which has already been born. We must take a stand on God's side by Scriptural conviction.

  3.   How are we to defend the right of babies to live?

    a.   Certainly not by violence or hatred.

    b.   We must preach and teach in our churches.

        1.   We must not be afraid to speak to others about our convictions.

        2.   We must teach our children to have moral principles and convictions based upon the Word of God, not upon popular opinion.

    c.   We can make our voices and convictions known by writing letters to those in governmental positions of authority.

    d.   God will help us be a strong and mighty army which will stand for the most basic of all needs of children—the right to live.

B.   Children need parents who know and love the Lord.

  1.   Christian parents must let their children know that they love the Lord.

  2.   Children most often follow the steps of their parents. We must take great care that our steps do not lead our children away from a love for the Lord.

  3.   Christian parents should teach often in the home about the goodness of God and lead children to love the Lord with all their heart, soul and mind, for this is the first and greatest commandment. Matthew 22:37-38 _____

_____

_____

C. Children need to be brought to a saving knowledge of Christ at a young age.

    1.   Read and record Matthew 19:14. _____

            _____

            _____

        a.   Jesus taught us to encourage little children to come to Him.

        b.   Approximately 80 percent of all Christians today trusted Christ before they reached the age of 20. (You can check this out in your own church or perhaps even in your Sunday School class.)

        c.   As a person grows older it becomes more and more difficult to convince him of his need for Christ as Savior.

    2.   We must remain faithful in the business of winning boys and girls to Christ.

        a.   We do this through Sunday School, bus ministries and vacation Bible schools, but no place is more effective than in the home.

        b.   The devil is after the hearts, lives and souls of young people. He uses every attractive device "in the book" to turn them away from Christ.

        c.   We must learn to stand against the wiles of the devil in defense of our children.

D. Children need to be loved and given a loving, secure home.

    1.   In many cases we are too concerned with providing materially for our children, and they are paying the price for our mistake.

        In many homes children are left alone for long periods of time as mothers and father pursue careers and hobbies.

    2.   Children thrive on love and attention.

        a.   They must be nurtured as carefully as a gardener tends his flowers.

        b.   Read Titus 2:4. What does this verse speak about? _____

            _____

            _____

        c.   God can help us not to be too busy to spend time loving our children.

            1.   We should show them our love.

            2.   We should verbalize our love.

E. Children need to be corrected Biblically and lovingly for their willful times of disobedience.

    1.   God commanded children to obey their parents. (Ephesians 6:1)

        a.   According to God it is a serious matter when children willfully disobey.

        1.   They are growing the seeds of rebellion that will bring them much damage and harm later in life.

        2.   A child who does not learn respect for authority at home will have a lot of trouble respecting authority later in life.

    b.   As we teach our children respect for authority, we must examine our own lives to see if we as parents have the proper respect for authority.

        1.   It is difficult to teach children to respect authority if we argue with the police officer or dispute our boss at work.

        2.   Parents must make sure they are setting the proper example at home, on the job, in the community, and even at church, when it comes to the matter of authority.

2.   Children must never be abused; they must receive love-motivated and Bible-guided discipline.

    a.   Read Proverb 19:18 and Proverb 29:15 and 17.

    b.   What do these verses teach? _____

_____

_____

    c.   Loving correction produces character and discipline in the lives of young people.

F.   Children need to be instructed in points of character and wisdom.

1.   Proverb 22:6 commands that we train our children in the way they should go in life.

    a.   This means we are to lead them onto the right path.

    b.   We must start when they are young. Proverb 20:11 _____

_____

_____

2.   Good character isn't part of a child's natural makeup.

    a.   Children are born with the same sin nature that we possess. They must be instructed and trained in proper behavior.

    b.   It is still very important and proper to instruct children that good manners demonstrate proper behavior.

    c.   The home is the ideal place to teach and to practice manners.

3.   Wisdom is taking what you know and applying it to your daily life.

    a.   The Book of Proverbs offers instruction in many different kinds of wisdom.

    b.   As a parent, challenge yourself to study the Book of Proverbs and instruct your children in wisdom.

4. Character is taught to children by simply demanding that the child do what is right until it becomes part of his nature.
    a. Things like picking up the clothes from the floor, putting toys away, cleaning up his own mess, brushing teeth, bathing daily, earning spending money, spending carefully, and caring for one's clothing are points of good character that can be taught by faithfully following through until the child does these things out of habit.
    b. Remember though, you will never have success in teaching a child to do anything more than what you are willing to do yourself. One must first have good character to teach good character!

G. Children need Godly examples and role models set before them which they can follow.
    1. Look carefully at Psalm 71:17-18.
        a. Notice in verse 17, King David says, *"I have **declared** thy wonderous works."*
        b. In verse 18, he asks the Lord not to forsake him until, *"I have **shewed** thy strength unto this generation."*
    2. We must take great care today in setting examples for our children.
        a. We too must pray that we can "show" this generation the strength of God and strive to "declare" His wondrous works to our children.
        b. Perhaps we have such a problem of rebellious youth because many Christian parents don't live their faith when they are outside the walls of the local church.
        c. The time for setting Godly examples before children is today!
            1. Children need direction.
            2. They should find that direction by following closely in our steps.
            3. Read what God said about Abraham in Genesis 18:18-19 and record your thoughts. _____

            _____

            _____

III. HOW TO MAINTAIN A HAPPY MARRIAGE

Anyone of legal age can get married. Keeping the flame of marriage glowing warmly over the years takes some degree of tending. How can we keep the fire burning?

A. Keep romance alive.
    1. Romance is the missing element in many marriages.
        a. It requires an investment of time to keep the

romance alive, but the return is certainly
worth the investment.

2.   Don't miss the principle taught in Luke 6:38. _____

_____

_____

   a.   If you want to be loved, you must first be
        willing to give love. And you must give it in
        the same amount you desire to receive it.
   b.   Every marriage needs to be filled with
        expressions of love, for love is the bond that
        holds two hearts together over the years.

3.   Accept your marriage partner as he or she is.
   a.   Are you negative, critical or uncomplimentary
        toward your spouse? If so, you're not doing
        very much to foster romance.
   b.   Stop trying to mold your husband or wife into
        what you want them to be. Learn to look for
        the good in the life of your partner and you'll
        find some.

4.   Admire your mate publicly.
   a.   Show your love, appreciation and admiration
        with little gifts and words of expression.
   b.   When you do this in public, it has an even
        greater effect upon your partner.
   c.   Look at the life of your partner and find
        something everyday to compliment. In so
        doing you are adding fuel to the fire of
        romance.

5.   Be amorous toward your mate.
   a.   Find ways to show your love. Don't be like the
        fellow who went with his wife to the pastor's
        office for marriage counseling. The wife
        complained that her husband never verbalized
        his love for her. When the pastor asked him if
        this was true, he said that it was. The pastor
        was somewhat surprised and asked the
        gentleman why he never told his wife he loved
        her. To this question the man replied, "Pastor, I
        told my wife at the altar 20 years ago that I
        loved her. If I ever change my mind I'll let her
        know."
   b.   We must not only say it, we must also show it!
        Remember, the Lord has shown His great love
        for us by giving His only Son. We cannot truly
        love without some "giving" being involved.
        Giving is the visible evidence of love.
   c.   Invest in your marriage. Unexpected gifts,
        cards, dinners out, flowers, out of town trips,
        etc., will certainly fuel the fire of romance.
   d.   Like any fire left unattended, the fire of a
        romantic relationship will die if you don't keep
        adding fuel.

IV. AVOIDING THE TRAP OF ADULTERY

Read Proverbs 5:1-23. This chapter is a gold mine of Bible principles which, when applied, will help you avoid the awful and damaging trap of adultery. In verse number one, the Bible calls our attention to *wisdom*. (Wisdom is learning how to apply Bible principles to life's situations.) The verses following give seven important principles to help Christians avoid the trap of Satan called unfaithfulness.

A. The consequences of adultery.

1. As with any trap, there is bait.
    a. The lure of adultery is appealing and tantilizing.
    b. Proverb 5:3 shows how the temptation to be unfaithful is presented by our enemy, the devil, as that which is attractive.

2. To see the whole picture, read verse 4.
    a. The end of an affair is bitterness.
    b. The trap of unfaithfulness begins with "oil and honey" and ends with "bitterness and wormwood."
    c. Wormwood is poison! An affair is as deadly as poison.

3. The story of King David's affair with Bathsheba presents a true illustration of this principle.
    a. David's sin of adultery brought him only moments of pleasure and years of bitterness and sorrow.
    b. It caused him grief and pain; it was poison to his soul.

4. Many people think they have no alternative but to remain in an exasperating marriage. Marriage doesn't have to be that way.
    a. Proverbs 5 teaches that the best plan is to enjoy an exciting, enjoyable and exhilarating marriage with our own spouse! (Proverbs 5:18-19)
    b. One cannot enjoy this kind of marriage while ignoring the principles of Proverbs, chapter 5.

B. There is the principle of separation.

1. Proverb 5:8 teaches the importance of staying away from all that is temptation.
    a. Don't toy and flirt with adultery.
    b. All sin begins first as temptation. To avoid sin you must stay away from the temptations that lead to sin.
    c. II Timothy 2:22 says, *"Flee youthful lusts."* In other words, don't play with fire! It's better to flee than to run the risk of getting burned!

2. Adultery is a sin that begins in the heart.
    a. Keep your heart right with God and filled with proper thoughts. Matthew 5:28 _____

_____

    b.   Learn to be faithful in your heart to avoid the trap of adultery.

    c.   Read the account of Potiphar's wife trying to entice Joseph into an affair (recorded in Genesis 39). Rather than "fall," Joseph decided to "flee." How wise we would be to do the same thing if temptation ever surrounds us.

C.   The principle of commitment.

    1.   Proverb 5:15 teaches a positive principle.

        a.   We are told to *"drink waters out of thine own cistern."*

        b.   But what does this mean? Every Jewish home had its own cistern to hold water. The cistern provided refreshment and satisfied thirst. Likewise, the Bible instructs married couples to find their satisfaction and refreshment with each other. That is far better than stealing water from the cistern of another.

    2.   Learn to be commited to one another.

        a.   Commitment to faithfulness is part of the marriage vow. We promise to be faithful till "death do us part."

        b.   If you didn't lie in your vow to God, you must keep your commitment. Let that promise to God guard your heart against the trap of the devil.

    3.   Just as the water of a cistern had to be kept fresh, so the waters of marriage must be kept fresh and flowing. Just remember to keep putting effort into the freshness of your marriage relationship.

D.   The principle of satisfaction.

    1.   Proverb 5:19 teaches us to be satisfied with our spouse.

        a.   The message of God is very clear!

        b.   He wants married life to be enjoyable and exciting.

    2.   The thief that often steals romance from married life is a thing called discontentment.

        a.   The Bible says, *"Be content, be satisfied."*

        b.   You are easy prey for the devil when you grow dissatisfied with your spouse.

        c.   Here is the great danger with soap operas, romance novels and pornography. These are the types of things the devil uses to create dissatisfaction with one's mate and to stir up the desire for someone more exciting.

        d.   Learn to guard your eyes, your heart and your mind from that which can lead to dissatisfaction with your partner.

E.   The principle of watchfulness in Proverbs chapter 5 says God is watching us. Note verse 21. _____

_____

_____

1.   There is not a day that God isn't watching. Our deeds are always before Him! We can hide from our spouse, our parents, our friends and our neighbors, but not from God. God sees! Do you want the Lord to be ashamed or do you want to please Him and live in such a way as to bring glory to His name? One way to achieve this goal is to build a happy home.

2.   Keeping a marriage fresh and exiting takes a certain amount of energy and care, but the happiness and satisfaction that follows is worth every hour invested.

V.   WHAT TO DO IF YOUR MARRIAGE IS ALREADY IN TROUBLE

Many married people get discouraged with books on marriage. Many marriage-related books deal with the subject from the standpoint of those who have a healthy home and want to keep it that way. Sometimes there is little advice offered to those who may already be troubled.

The last part of this lesson looks at what to do when a marriage is troubled. Keep in mind this is directed toward Christian marriages. Those without Christ need first to understand their need of salvation. Without Jesus, the solid Rock, there will be no lasting foundation upon which to build. There are seven things you can do which might help when you have a problem at home.

A.   Face up to the fact that there is a problem.

1.   Don't pretend everything is all right if it isn't.
   a.   Ignoring problems and strife won't make them go away.
   b.   No one can be helped until first they will admit that a problem exists.

2.   Set aside whatever time is needed to talk to your spouse in a Biblical manner.
   a.   That means first to *"speak the truth in love."* (Ephesians 4:15)
   b.   Ephesians 4:29 commands that no corrupt communication proceed out of the Christian's mouth. What kind of communication is corrupt? _____

_____

_____

3.   Face the problem. Proverb 28:13 _____

_____

_____

B.   Study the problem with great care.

   1.   Be honest and specific about the problem but don't cast all the blame on your partner.

      a.   For every problem there is a cause, and to every problem there is a solution.

      b.   You must take the time to find the cause or causes of marriage problems or you'll never find the solution.

   2.   Make a list of the causes of the problem.

      a.   As you discover them, arrange the list according to the priorities.

      b.   Tackle the most serious problems first. You will be surprised how many of the smaller things will then vanish. Why? Because they were symptoms of the greater problem. If you take care of the most serious things first, you will find that many of the smaller symptoms will disappear.

   3.   As you and your mate open your hearts and talk in honesty and love, you mustn't be tempted to deny the problems that your spouse sees and you don't.

      a.   Marriage is oneness. If the wife has a problem, the husband must also share it, for they are no longer two, they are one in the bond of marriage.

      b.   Don't fall into the trap of denial!

C.   Be willing to accept the responsibility.

   1.   This is the major snag in working out most marriage problems.

      a.   No one wants to take the responsibility.

      b.   This attitude can be traced to the garden of Eden when Adam blamed Eve and Eve blamed the serpent.

   2.   Someone must be willing to make the first move toward correction.

      a.   In the garden of Eden, when Adam and Eve sinned against God, their sin separated them from God. Who made the first move toward reconciliation? It was God! The One who had been wronged was willing to make the first move to correct the problem.

      b.   It is a Godly attitude to be willing to take the responsibility for reconciliation.

   3.   There is certainly nothing spiritual about pride and stubbornness.

      a.   Whatever can be done to bring about a remedy for marriage problems should be done.

      b.   If you always wait for your spouse to make the first move, you may lose your marriage.

D.   Be willing to adjust your life in whatever way will speed a solution to the problem.

1. You cannot change your partner against his or her
    will, but you can change your own attitudes and
    behavior.

    a. The Christian has the power of God available
        to help change his life in anyway necessary
        and helpful.

    b. To say otherwise is to deny the power and
        ability of God.

2. For instance, the Bible says, *"Husbands, love your
    wives...."* This isn't a suggestion; it's a Biblical
    command!

    a. God would never give His children a
        command without also giving the power and
        understanding to obey the command.

    b. Be willing to open your heart to the Lord's
        examination. Let Him uncover, through the
        Holy Spirit's conviction, faults in action,
        attitude, character and deeds. Then seek His
        help and power to change them.

E. Learn to accept and love your spouse as God loves him.

    1. Nobody is perfect. We must learn, therefore, to
        accept and love our mate along with any small
        imperfections he or she may possess.

        a. Read Colossians 3:13 and write your summary
            of this verse's teaching. _____

            _____

            _____

        b. God loves us as we are. We must learn to love
            and accept our spouse so that we aren't led
            into the sin of dissatisfaction.

        c. People can be loved into change must faster
            than they can be forced to change.

F. Study everything you can find in the Bible related to
    marriage and the home. Then walk in God's principles to
    the very best of your ability.

    1. There is no effective way to build a happy home
        without practicing the principles of God's Word.
        Psalm 119:24 _____

        _____

        _____

    2. God's Word is the counselor who will teach us how
        to live with one another in harmony and joy.

        a. Since God is the designer of marriage, doesn't
            it seem logical that He is the one best
            qualified to write the book on marriage?

        b. Too many troubled Christians today read
            everything BUT the Bible! It is God's Word that
            will guide us into perfect truth. We stumble
            and fall when we try to walk without the light
            of God's Word. Psalm 119:105 _____

_____

_____

3. The Bible is the place where we find all the duties and obligations of family members spelled out simply and clearly.

a. For a sample of this truth read Colossians 3:12-23 and write principles found in this passage relating to your marriage and home relationships. _____

_____

_____

b. Ignoring and rejecting Bible principles always leads to disaster, but following the Word of God leads to prosperity in marriage.

G. Learn to put the accent on the positive things in your home and marriage.

1. This is simple, yet vital.
a. Isn't it strange how quick we are to see the faults in others while overlooking our own?
b. When you do this, it's an indication that you need your own heart adjusted.

2. Stop dwelling on the negative, and emphasize that which is good and positive.
a. Hebrews 3:13 commands that we *"exhort one another daily."* Do you do that at your house? Do you try to encourage each other in some area every day? If not, begin to practice this principle as soon as you can.
b. One of the most important duties in marriage is to uplift and encourage one another.
c. Read Ecclesiastes 4:9-11. What does this wonderful passage teach? _____

_____

_____

d. Remember, the fastest way to be encouraged personally is to get involved in encouraging others. *"Give, and it shall be given you!"*

SUMMARY: According to Ephesians 5:32-33, the marriage of a Christian man and a Christian woman is to be a daily example of Christ's great love for His own. When we fail to display that testimony before others, we grieve the Lord.

Marriage can be a little bit of heaven upon earth. God designed it to be that way. A home can grow in love and happiness over the years, but not without work and effort. Just as any garden will die for lack of tending, a marriage will fail if it isn't tended with things like love, patience, kindness, mercy, compassion and forgiveness.

The first seeds of destruction could best be called the seeds of neglect. It's the little things that we fail to do that most often lead to a less than satisfactory marriage.

Why settle for less than God wanted your home to be? Forget the past, look with renewed zeal to the future and learn to walk with God's help and strength. Your marriage can be a "harbor of hopelessness" or a "haven of joy." It all depends upon where you set your course and steer the ship.

Happy homes and joy-filled marriages don't just happen. They are the result of two people who will take the time to study the Word of God and practice the principles that lead to a growing and loving relationship. Marriage can get sweeter as the years go by. The sugar has to be added one day at a time!

REFLECTIONS: Answer the following questions individually or in class. Give careful attention to your answers. This exercise is what the Bible refers to as meditation. Think on these things....

1. What is God's basic plan for the formation of a home?

   _____

   _____

2. What does the Bible mean when it says that a husband is to leave his father and mother and cleave unto his wife?

   _____

   _____

3. Briefly summarize the duty of the husband and the wife individually, according to the Bible. In what book and chapter of the Bible can this be found?

   _____

   _____

4. List the basic needs of children.

   _____

   _____

5. What is character? How is it taught?

   _____

   _____

6. What is the missing element in many marriages today? What can be done to keep its spark alive?

   _____

   _____

7. How does the sin of adultery begin? What can we do to guard ourselves against this sin?

   _____

   _____

8. If we are to find a solution to any problem in our marriage, what must we do first?

   _____

   _____

9. Where must we learn to place the "accent" in our homes? How can we do this?

   _____

   _____

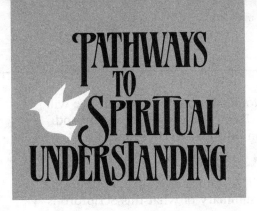

LESSON 20

Our Adversary the Devil

MAIN SCRIPTURES:
I PETER 5:6-11; LUKE 22:31-32
EPHESIANS 6:10-18; ISAIAH 14:12-15;
LUKE 10:18; REVELATION 20:10

LESSON AIM: To lead to a proper and Scriptural understanding of our enemy, the devil. To understand his power and his unholy desires. To learn how to overcome his temptations and live in victory. To lead to the confidence that he is already a defeated foe.

SUGGESTED MEMORY VERSES: I Peter 5:8; James 4:7; II Corinthians 2:11; Ephesians 4:27; John 10:10

OVERVIEW:

I. A BRIEF HISTORY OF THE DEVIL

II. SATAN'S THREE BATTLEGROUNDS

III. THE DEVIL'S BATTLE PLAN FOR OUR DEFEAT

IV. HOW TO DEFEND YOURSELF AGAINST THE DEVIL

INTRODUCTION: This lesson covers a very famous personality. First, a little about his character: He's a murderer, a thief, a gossip, a slanderer and a liar. He rules over a vast territory which stretches around the globe. His main business is dealing in human misery and sorrow. He's the avowed enemy of all Christians and the opposer of all of the work of God, whatever it may be. His nature will not change, and if he had his way all churches would be closed today! Of course,

this is a description of Satan.

The number of Christians who always smile a little when the doctrine of the devil is taught is surprising. Perhaps we don't really know him as he is. Many don't really believe he exists at all. He would be most happy to keep his work and identity concealed. He doesn't want God's people to know about him, or even to believe in him. He's a thief. All thieves want to carry out their business under the cover of darkness. So it is with the devil.

The Apostle Paul warns Christians (in II Corinthians 2:11) not to be ignorant of the devices of the devil. If we are willfully ignorant of him, he will find it very easy to take advantage of us with any one of his many deadly, destructive devices.

Military experts say in time of battle the best way to defeat the enemy is to know all you can about him. You need to know who he is, where he's going and what it is he wants to do in our lives. We mustn't hide our head in the sands of unconcern.

While we pretend the devil is a mythological character leftover from the dark ages, he is busy about his ambition of destruction and opposition. This lesson will not spend a lot of time on the subject of the devil's creation and his original fall from heaven. Much of that information has been taught for many years. However, you should read Isaiah 14:12-15 to lay the foundation for this lesson. We will spend our time studying the devil's work in our lives, home and churches today and what we can do today to overcome his influence.

(Where lines are provided after a Scripture reference, look up the verse and write a one sentence summary of what this Scripture is saying to you.)

I.   A BRIEF HISTORY OF THE DEVIL

In order to lay a foundation for the rest of the lesson, we will briefly cover the history of the devil.

A.   Satan's beginning.

1.   Satan is a spirit created by God.
a.   Colossians 1:16 _____

_____

_____

b.   The devil is one of the invisible creations mentioned in Colossians 1:16.

2.   His original standing is described in Ezekiel 28:12-15.
a.   Satan was created by God as an "anointed cherub."
b.   He was exalted to a higher position than most of the other angels. (Ezekiel 28:14)
c.   He was full of wisdom and beauty. (Ezekiel 28:12)
d.   But his heart was lifted up against God. This is the sin of pride. (Ezekiel 28:17)
e.   From this chapter we can determine that God made angels with a will and the ability to choose.

3.   Satan's expulsion from heaven is related in Isaiah 14:12-15.
a.   He was cast out from the presence of God because of his prideful heart.
b.   His realm is now the earth. Jesus never claimed this world as His kingdom, for this world is the kingdom of darkness.

B.   The devil is a literal personality.

1.   Just as many people misunderstand the personality of the Holy Spirit, many people fail to understand the personality of Satan.
a.   Satan isn't just some force of evil at work in the world today; he's a living being.
b.   He's a spirit rather than a "fleshly" being, but he's a very real personality.
c.   The story of the temptation of Jesus recorded in Matthew 4:1-11 finds the Lord Jesus and Satan in a face to face meeting. Jesus wasn't

speaking to some nonexistent force; He was
speaking directly with Satan.

    d.   Satan has all the characteristics of personality
including emotions, intellect, the ability to
speak and to act. He's a real person.

    e.   Unlike God however, he's limited in his ability
and realm. For instance, nowhere in the Bible
does it say the devil has the power to be in
more than one place at one time. He's a
powerful personality, but he's a limited
personality.

C.   Some names the Bible gives to the devil.

   1.   He's called the god of this world in II Corinthians
4:4

   2.   He's called the dragon, the serpent, the devil and
Satan.
    a.   Revelation 12:9.
    b.   The words "dragon" and "serpent" tells us
what about his character and nature? _____

       _____

       _____

   3.   He can be tranformed into "an angel of light."
    a.   II Corinthians 11:14.
    b.   He can transform himself into something he is
not!

   4.   He is called "a roaring lion."
    a.   I Peter 5:8.
    b.   What does this tell us about his work? _____

       _____

       _____

D.   The devil's kingdom companions.

   1.   In Matthew 12:22-28 Jesus is seen casting out
devils. Notice the plurality of this statement. He
wasn't casting out the devil, but ***devils.***
    a.   These devils are sometimes called demons.
They are the angels that participated in Satan's
revolt in Heaven. They, too, were cast out and
now do Satan's bidding.
    b.   The Book of Revelation, chapter 12 verse 4,
speaks of Satan as "drawing" the third part of
the stars of heaven when he fell. Many
teachers of the Bible believe this refers to the
number of fallen angels that are today called
demons.
    c.   No one knows how many that is, but it could
be as many as 30 or 40 million based upon
what we read in Revelation 5:11.
       1.   In this chapter the Apostle John recorded
his vision and what he saw taking place
around the throne in Heaven.

2. Verse 11 records the fact that John heard
    the voice of "many angels." He then gave
    a figure that equals 100 million.

3. It's only logical that if there are at least
    100 million angels still left in heaven
    which **weren't** cast out with Satan's
    rebellion, the one third that **were** cast
    out with the devil could easily number
    30 or 40 million.

II. SATAN'S THREE BATTLEGROUNDS

The Bible clearly teaches that the life of a Christian is lived
on the field of battle. II Timothy 2:3 says Christians are
soldiers. Ephesians 6:11 tells us that Christians are to *"put on
the whole armor of God, that ye may be able to stand
against the wiles of the devil."* In this spiritual battle there
are three fields where Christians engage in battle with the
devil.

A. The first is your own personal life.

    1. The devil wants to destroy the influence and the
        testimony of every Christian.
        a. It is God's people who do the work of God.
        b. If the devil can destroy lives and ruin
            testimonies no one will be effective in serving
            the Lord.
        c. It's easy to see the advantage he will gain if he
            is successful in this endeavor.

B. The next field of attack is the home.

    1. The devil wants to fill homes with turmoil and
        trouble.
        a. Why? Because the home is the basic unit of
            society.
            1. It's the place where children are trained.
            2. It's a place of strong influence upon the
                lives of others.
        b. If the devil can destroy homelife, he might also
            succeed in his goal of ruining the lives of our
            children. His motive and goal is that there not
            be another generation raised in Christian
            homes.

C. The third major field of attack is the Church.

    1. The devil is busy today in his goal of dividing and
        destroying local churches and their ministries.
        a. Why? Because the Church is the center for
            world evangelism and the place where God's
            people meet for instruction and
            encouagement.
        b. The church is the most important center of
            training outside of the home. The devil knows
            this and is waging a great attack today against
            pastors and churches.

III. THE DEVIL'S PLAN FOR OUR DEFEAT

Here is the heart of this lesson. We must understand how the devil works if we are to ever be successful in standing against him. We can never let down our guard against him. He works inwardly against us more than he does outwardly. Never forget that fact.

A.   The devil's devices against our lives.

    1.   He attacks through doubt.

        a.   Many people go through life without the wonderful assurance of their salvation.

        b.   Doubting is certainly of the devil; it always leads to a defeated life filled with discouragement.

        c.   Place your faith for assurance of salvation solely and completely upon the Word of God. God's Word cannot lie. Believe it because God has said it. Don't allow feelings to destroy your confidence and assurance. Read John 5:24 and John 10:28. Write I John 5:13 _____

        _____

        _____

    2.   The devil will attack with distance.

        a.   This means he will encourage you to live just a little further away from the Lord than you should.

        b.   Backsliding doesn't happen overnight. It's the result of weeks, months or even years of neglecting the things we ought to do.

        c.   The Bible says the night Jesus was betrayed in the garden *"Peter followed afar off."*

            1.   It wasn't too much later that he sat down with the wrong crowd of people.

            2.   Not long after he sat down with the wrong crowd of people he cursed and swore and denied that he even knew Jesus.

            3.   Do you see the progression of sin in this story? It all began when Peter followed *"afar off."*

        d.   As a Christian it is important that you follow the Lord as closely as you possibly can. It's when we lag behind that we're easy prey for the devil's attack.

    3.   The devil will sometimes attack with discouragement.

        a.   Discouragement has ruined more lives and hindered more of God's work than anything else.

        b.   Discouragement leads to a host of other sins.

            1.   It was when the children of Israel became discouraged that they murmured against

God and against Moses. The story is recorded in Numbers, chapter 21.

    2.   It was when Elijah got discouraged that he quit serving the Lord. His story is found in I Kings, chapter 19.

    c.   We must realize that God is greater than all circumstances.

        1.   God is always in complete control.

        2.   We need to learn to look to Him for help and strength in times of difficulty so the devil will not be able to discourage us.

        3.   When we allow ourselves to get discouraged, we are easy prey for the devil.

B.   The devil attacks our homes.

    1.   He attacks many homes with the snare of materialism.

        a.   The desire to acquire more and more material things has destroyed many good homes.

            1.   This very principle is taught in I Timothy 6:6-10.

            2.   Read this and write your observations. __

                _____

                _____

        b.   Materialism leads too easily into the bondage of excessive debt.

            1.   Very few Christians can have a happy home and marriage when they are bound by too much debt.

            2.   At all cost, you must learn to avoid this snare of the devil.

    2.   He attacks with busy-ness.

        a.   This is a very subtle way the devil destroys many homes. He simply encourages Christians to get involved in too many outside things.

        b.   We engage in hobbies, sports, clubs, classes, organizations, school activities, church work and many other things. It's easy to get over-burdened in our time commitments. When this happens, nothing we do gets our best. Usually our homelife will also suffer.

        c.   Make a list of priorities for your time.

            1.   Keep spiritual things close to the top.

            2.   Many times when it comes to being busy, people give up the work they do for the Lord and retain outside interest. This too, is the work of the devil.

            3.   We are not to forsake the church and the work of God for sports, hobbies, clubs and other such things that will reap no eternal dividends.

    3.   In many cases the devil finds an avenue of attack to

our homes through the television or stereo.

   a.   If you listen and write down the lyrics to much of today's popular music you would be shocked at what is being promoted.

       1.   Many of the most popular themes of music glorify immorality of all types, drugs, alcohol and rebellion against authority.

       2.   Even suicide is glorified in some music. In several towns, teenagers have taken their lives while listening to songs that glorify suicide as a peaceful way to escape problems and pay back those who have mistreated them.

       3.   We must see this as another way the devil is attacking the value system of our homes.

   b.   More and more television programming is damaging to home values.

       1.   What is being promoted in living color and sound is often shocking.

       2.   Would you invite a prostitute or drug addict into your home and allow them to teach your children about what they do?

       3.   Many nights that's just what we do through the medium of TV.

       4.   How many children hear their first swear words on television?

   c.   That is not to say we should destroy these devices and remove them from our homes. But we should watch and listen with care. We need to apply "Christian control" over that which comes into our family rooms.

4.   Sometimes the devil lays a trap for us called apathy.

   a.   It is easy to get so involved in other things that we soon care little for others.

   b.   Don't let the devil lure you and your family into the snare of apathy. We need to care not only about those who live within our own house but also those outside our home.

   c.   Apathy steals laborers. Much church work goes undone because some Christians have fallen into the trap of not caring. We must care for others or we will soon become easy prey for the devil.

5.   The devil destroys homelife through an attack upon character.

   a.   Good character doesn't come naturally; it must be taught and developed over the years.

   b.   Character is what you are when no one else is around. Character is doing right simply because it's the right thing to do.

   c.   Character consists of little things in life like

being on time, making your bed, cleaning up you own mess, paying your bills on time, eating the right foods, reading your Bible and praying each day, going to church even on a cold or rainy day, finishing what you start, giving your best to each project you undertake and many, many more such things.

d.   Character is something we must teach and practice at home.

e.   King David fell into sin with Bathsheba because he didn't exercise good character.

    1.   When he noticed her bathing while he strolled on his rooftop, he should have turned back to his room and minded his own business.

    2.   He didn't, and of course, this led him into temptation and eventually into the sin that wrecked his life.

f.   We must teach and practice good character at home. The devil will be waiting somewhere on the "rooftop" for us, and we must not be ignorant of his devices.

C.   The devil's plan of attack against the Church.

  1.   He will try *deception*.

    a.   There are more cults today than ever before. Most of the people today who are members of cults were at one time church members.

    b.   Those who have left an established church to join a cult, frequently say they were first attracted by the love and warmth of the cult's members.

    c.   We need to make sure our church is the kind of church where people feel welcome. It's possible to be too unfriendly, but it's impossible to be too friendly.

    d.   We must know what we believe and why we believe it lest the devil attack us through deception.

  2.   He often attacks the church services with *disruption*.

    a.   We cannot hope to see more people won to Christ in our church services if they cannot pay attention to the pastor while he is speaking.

    b.   This may seem trivial, but the devil is at work through disrupting our services.

    c.   Churches shouldn't be as quiet as a morgue, but neither should we sleep, talk, pass notes, or do other things while the services are taking place in God's house.

  3.   Sometimes the devil attacks the church through *diversion*.

    a.   That is, he endeavors to detour us from the

main business of the church, to busying ourselves with other works.

b. Think of the story of Nehemiah as he set about to rebuild the walls of Jerusalem.
    1. He was ordered by God to do this great work and was determined not to be hindered.
    2. Read Nehemiah 6:1-3 and record Nehemiah's answer to those who tried to divert his attention. _____

    _____

    _____

c. Be very careful not to be side-tracked in the work God has given us.
    1. Many churches have become social centers with the emphasis switched from ministry to fellowship.
    2. There is nothing wrong with fellowship. In fact, it's needful for spiritual health. But it isn't the only purpose for church.
    3. We need to keep the evangelism clear in our hearts as the priority of our church ministry.

4. One of the devil's favorite tactics is **division.**
    a. The devil is a master at "divide and conquer." He knows he can weaken the Church if he can pit one against another.
    b. He began using this approach against the church at Jerusalem in Acts, chapter 6.
        1. The Grecians rose up against the Hebrews and complained that favoritism was being shown to the Hebrew widows over the Grecian widows.
        2. The solution to this problem was the formation of the first board of deacons within the Church. The deacons were to help in the matter of widow's care.
        3. The important thing to remember in this story is how the devil tried to stop the Church by creating division.
    c. He wants you to be jealous, or offended, or to get your feelings hurt, or feel ignored. It is important that God's people grow above such feelings and see them as the work of the devil. His goal is to divide church members and to hinder the work and outreach of the Church in the community.
    d. If you stop to think about it, you will remember many times, perhaps even in your own experience at church, when the devil has worked just this way.
    e. We must not allow the devil to sow his seeds of discord. There is strength in unity. There is

power in the sweetness of fellowship.

5. He also uses *disloyalty*.
    a. Nothing is as heartbreaking as someone who is disloyal. What did the Apostle Paul say of a man named Deman in II Timothy 4:10? _____

    _____

    _____

    b. Part of a Christian's duty is to be loyal and faithful to the Church. He should be loyal in attendance, in giving, in support, in service and in defense of the Church.
    c. What if every member of your church were just like you? What kind of church would your church be?
    d. Churches aren't buildings, but people. The building is useless without God's people who meet within. If church work is to be effective in the cause Christ gave us, we need to be loyal.

IV. HOW TO DEFEND YOURSELF AGAINST THE DEVIL

We are engaged in a spiritual battle with Satan. In this battle we are not defenseless. God has given us His Word and taught us how to resist the devil. There are a number of things we can do to stand against the enemy of our lives, our homes and our churches.

A. Recognize temptation as the tool of Satan.

    1. All sin first begins as temptation.
        a. If we can learn to stand effectively against temptation we will save ourselves a lot of sorrow over sin.
        b. Temptation to do that which is evil never comes from God! James 1:13-14 _____

        _____

        _____

        c. God never "tests" His children with some temptation to do wrong. All temptation to sin comes from the devil. You need to know that and understand that so you can learn how to resist the devil.
    2. God has promised to provide a way of escape.
        a. I Corinthians 10:13 _____

        _____

        _____

        b. The problem is, often we don't take time to look for the way of escape that God has provided.
        c. If you don't learn to recognize temptation and look for the way of escape, you'll never be

242

successful in resisting the devil.

B.   To overcome the devil you must "walk in the light."

    1.   In John 10:10, Jesus calls the devil a thief.
        a.   No thief wants to come into the light. He wants to do his wicked business in the dark.
        b.   When you want to protect your house against burglars, one of the first things experts will tell you is to install more light around your property. This same principle holds true concerning your spiritual life.

    2.   We must learn to walk in the light.
        a.   I John 1:6-7 _____

_____

        b.   Jesus is the light of the world. (John 8:12) If we stay very close to Him we won't put ourselves in a position where the devil can easily attack us.
        c.   Stay close to the Lord. Spend time with Him every day in prayer and Bible study. In so doing, you are spreading more light around your life. It will be more and more difficult for the devil to attack you. Remember Psalm 119:11. _____

_____

_____

C.   Learn to watch, as would a guard.

    1.   One of the most important points of defense is detection.
        a.   Read Matthew 24:43. In this verse Jesus says a homeowner will do two things if he knows a thief is coming.
        b.   He will watch, and he will be ready!

    2.   Learn to stand guard over your life, especially at your weakest points.
        a.   All of us have a point at which we are the weakest. It is vital to be on guard against the devil's temptation.
        b.   Watch that you do not open the door of temptation to the devil. Never put yourself in a position or in a place where it would be easy for you to fall into temptation. Ephesians 4:27

_____

_____

        c.   Remember what James 1:14 teaches.

D.   Become skilled in the use of the only weapon of warfare God has given us.
    1.   That weapon is the Bible, the Word of God. Ephesians 6:17 _____

_____

_____

2. The weapon is powerful.
   a. Hebrews 4:12 _____

   _____

   _____

   b. II Corinthians 10:3-4 teaches us that our weapon is not a physical weapon, but a spiritual weapon. We are also told in this passage of Scripture that it is mighty!

   c. When the devil tempted Jesus in the wilderness, Jesus turned him back by saying, _"It is written...."_

   d. Read the Word, study it, hide it away in your heart, that you, too, will be able to turn the devil back when he attacks.

   e. The devil is no more afraid of a Christian who doesn't use his Bible than a thief would be of a homeowner with a cap pistol.
      1. We must take seriously the admonition in II Timothy 2:15 to study our Bibles.
      2. We need to be skilled in the use of the _"sword of the Spirit"_ if we hope to be the victor in our battles with the devil.

SUMMARY: During his last days upon earth, the Apostle Paul recorded these words in II Timothy 4:6-7, _"For I am now ready to be offered, and the time of my departure is at hand. I have fought a good fight, I have finished my course, I have kept the faith."_ What was the fight he had engaged in? It was the fight of the faith. Paul was a faithful and committed soldier in this spiritual battle.

He went on to say, in verse 8, _"Henceforth there is laid up for me a crown of righteousness, which the Lord, the righteous judge, shall give me at that day...."_ We are in the same spiritual battle. We must learn to be good soldiers. A good soldier is one who does not give up in the heat of the battle. He knows who the enemy is and will fight only his enemy.

Today we seem to have a real problem determining who the enemy really is. We have allowed the devil to divide the people of God until we are now so busy fighting among our own little camps that we are losing the real battle. The battle is the Lord's. Renew your commitment to resist the devil at every level of his attack. To do so is to stand in defense of your life, your homes and your church. The devil is a defeated foe. His end is already revealed in Revelation 20:10. Thank God, we are on the winning side! Resist the devil and he will flee from you.

REFLECTIONS: Answer the following questions individually or in class. Give careful attention to your answers. This exercise is what the Bible refers to as meditation. Think on these things....

1. What kind of being is Satan? How was he created?

   _____

   _____

2. What was his sin? What were the results?

   _____

   _____

3. List at least three different names the Bible gives to Satan.

   _____

   _____

4. In the Bible we find many cases of work being carried out by demons. Who are these demons? Where did they come from?

   _____

   _____

5. What are Satan's three basic battlegrounds?

   _____

   _____

6. List at least three ways the devil attacks the individual child of God.

   _____

   _____

7. List at least three ways he attacks the home.

   _____

   _____

8. List three of his devices against the work of the Church.

   _____

   _____

9. How does all sin begin? Where does this take place?

   _____

   _____

10. How can we defeat the devil in this first attack upon us?

   _____

   _____